THE CRUISING GUIDE TO

CARIBBEAN MARINAS AND SERVICES

By Ashley Scott and Nancy Scott

1st Edition

J. Raycroft

J. Raycroft

CRUISING GUIDE TO
CARIBBEAN
MARINAS AND
SERVICES

Published by
Cruising Guide Publications, Inc.
P.O. Box 1017, Dunedin, FL 34697-1017
(727) 733-5322 Fax (727) 734-8179
(800) 330-9542
info@cruisingguides.com
Website: www.cruisingguides.com

Author: Ashley Scott and Nancy Scott
Art Direction: Jessica Stevens, Affinity Design Group
Photography: Jim Raycroft, Jeff Fisher, Simon Charles, A.J. Blake, William Houghton

Color Charts: Courtesy of Simon Charles, Chris Doyle,
Explorer Chart Books, www.explorercharts.com

Advertising/Marketing Director: Maureen Larroux

Administration: Janet Joyce and Connie Warner

Front Cover Design: Michael O'Keene, Affinity Design Group

Front Cover Photography
Top: Jim Raycroft, left: Jim Scheiner,
Right: Courtesy of Tortola Yacht Services

This guide is intended for use with offical navigational charts. Every effort has been made to describe conditions accurately, however, the publisher makes no warranty, expressed or implied, for any errors or for any omissions in this publication. The sailor must use this guide only in conjunction with charts and other navigational aids and not place undue credence in the accuracy of this guide. This guide is not to be used for navigational purposes.

First Edition
Printed in the USA
ISBN 0-944428-60-6

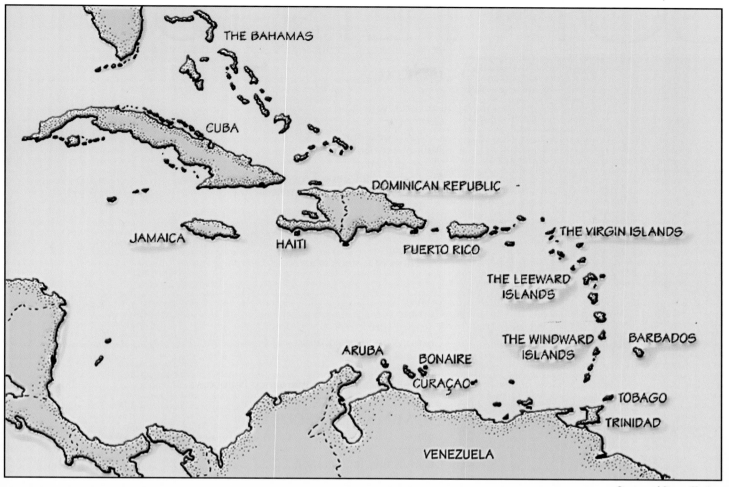

Courtesy of Simon Charles

Do you want to get away from stress of your job, the commute, the dreary weather, and the barrage of world news? Do you want to just get on a boat and sail away to the warm, turquoise waters of the Caribbean? That is a goal that is not so far-fetched. Many people have changed their lifestyles and either taken a long sabbatical, or taken an early retirement, purchased a seaworthy vessel and headed for the warmth, sun and balmy breezes of the Caribbean. This guide is a valuable tool for yachties heading south.

Cruising Guide Publications has been publishing guides to the waters of the Caribbean for over twenty years. We publish nine guides covering the superb sailing destinations from Cuba down the arch of the eastern Caribbean to Venezuela and the ABC islands. In this guide we have focused on the marinas and marine services for this part of the Caribbean. This book gives cruising yachts a comprehensive directory to plan their cruise in advance, knowing where to find marinas that can accommodate their size vessel. Incorporated is information on what paperwork is needed for customs and immigration clearance and which harbors are ports of entry. Telephone area codes and emergency numbers for each island are important to know before you go. There are several countries represented in the islands, each with different currency, telephones and language. Sail prepared with this book as your reference along with your cruising guides.

With this guide you can be in Puerto Rico and find information on haul-out facilities in Trinidad, or St. Martin. You will be able to contact marinas, boatyards, and all types of marine services for the entire island chain. Should a crew member become ill you will know where to find the closest hospital. *Caribbean Marinas and Services* is an ideal companion to our popular cruising guides of the islands.

We encourage our readers to send us information and suggestions for the next edition. It is our readers feedback that keeps our guides the best guides to yachting in the eastern Caribbean.

Bon Voyage!

CONTENTS

J. Raycroft

J. Raycroft

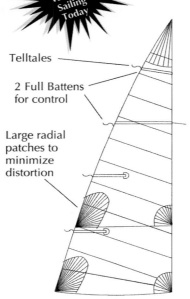
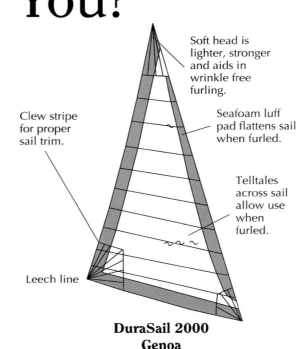

  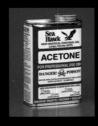   

BAHAMAS

J. Raycroft

A Tropical Nation of Countless Islands and Clear Turquoise Sea

Culture

The Bahamas, located due east of Florida's East Coast, are a sailing haven ranked with some of the best in the world. Crystal blue waters, excellent snorkeling and diving, white sand beaches and islands close in proximity to each other have helped the Nation of the Bahamas to thrive as a major tourist destination. The Bahamas consist of over 700 islands; 5,383 square miles. Much of the Bahamas are surrounded by shallow, crystal clear water, which is why they were named by their Spanish conquerors as the "great shallow seas". Beyond the shelf of limestone, sand, and coral heads, the depth of the sea is immense. To add to the contrast, the average elevation of these islands is only 100 feet.

Historically, the islands were inhabited by a group of Indians called the Lucayans. When the Spanish happened upon the Bahamas whilst in search of India, they met with the Lucayans. Within 25 years, the Bahamian natives were extinct having been subject to European diseases, sold into slavery, and sometimes starving to death. However, it soon became clear that these islands were not as useful as originally anticipated. Without gold or sufficient topsoil for crops, the Bahamas were deemed pretty much useless by the Spanish. It wasn't until the 17th century that British settlers came to live on the islands, known as the Eleutheran Adventurers. From this point on, the history of Bahamian prosperity is somewhat sordid.

Toward the end of the 17th century, the Bahamian age of piracy began. Because the Bahamas at that time were virtually lawless, it was a perfect place for the plundering and looting of other ships. In addition, the complex geography of the islands allowed for sneak attacks and the much reputed burying of treasure. Around the late 18th century, after piracy had been mostly eradicated, American colonists who were still British Loyalists began to settle in to the Bahamas. In 1783, aided by a South Carolina militia, the settlers were able to force the Spanish out of the region for good. Soon after, the Civil War began, and the Bahamian economy would prosper by aiding British ships to trade with the confederacy for goods such as cotton. The goods that they received in return from the British ships would then be sold at incredible profit. When the Civil War was over, the economy took a dive, but only to boom again in the early 20th century with the onset of prohibition in the United States. The Bahamas were a close enough port to the U.S. to smuggle mass amounts of alcohol in and out, and as a result, Nassau Harbour was increased in size to accommodate such rum-running. When prohibition was over, the Bahamas would hit its last economic low until the early 1960's when Cuba was closed to American tourists. The Bahamas were finally discovered as a fine vacation spot, and the hotels, restaurants, and cruise ships would come soon after. On July 10th, 1973, the Bahamas finally became its own nation. Since then,

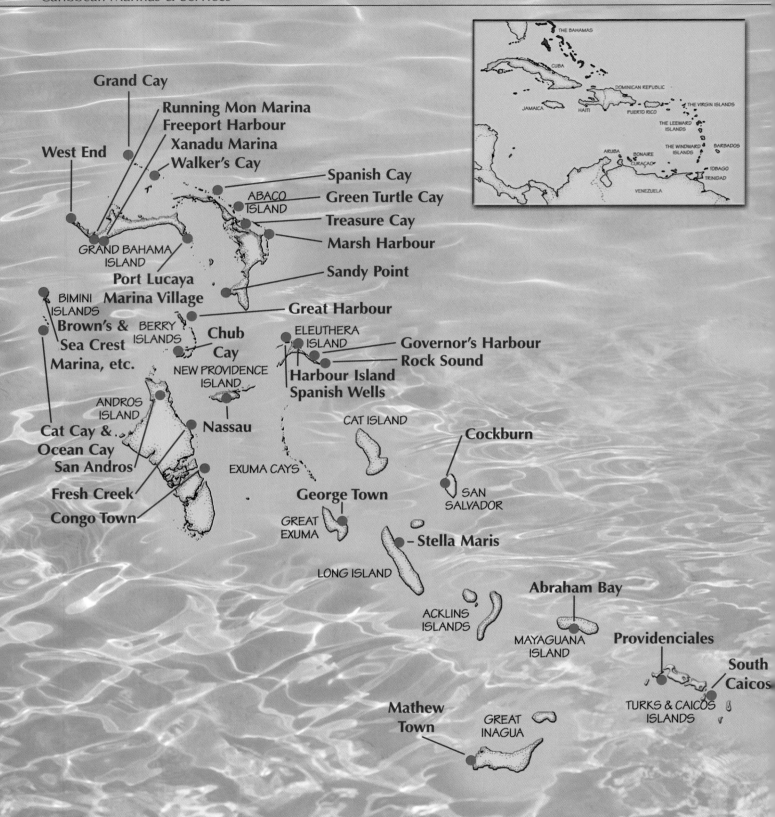

Grand Cay
Running Mon Marina
Freeport Harbour
Xanadu Marina
Walker's Cay
West End
Spanish Cay
Green Turtle Cay
ABACO ISLAND
Treasure Cay
Marsh Harbour
GRAND BAHAMA ISLAND
Port Lucaya
Sandy Point
BIMINI ISLANDS
Marina Village
Great Harbour
Brown's &
BERRY ISLANDS
Chub Cay
ELEUTHERA ISLAND
Governor's Harbour
Sea Crest
Rock Sound
Marina, etc.
NEW PROVIDENCE ISLAND
Harbour Island
Spanish Wells
ANDROS ISLAND
CAT ISLAND
Cockburn
Cat Cay &
Nassau
Ocean Cay
SAN SALVADOR
San Andros
EXUMA CAYS
George Town
Fresh Creek
Congo Town
GREAT EXUMA
Stella Maris
LONG ISLAND
Abraham Bay
ACKLINS ISLANDS
Providenciales
MAYAGUANA ISLAND
South Caicos
TURKS & CAICOS ISLANDS
Mathew Town
GREAT INAGUA

THE BAHAMAS
CUBA
DOMINICAN REPUBLIC
THE VIRGIN ISLANDS
JAMAICA
HAITI
PUERTO RICO
THE LEEWARD ISLANDS
THE WINDWARD ISLANDS
BARBADOS
ARUBA
BONAIRE
CURAÇAO
TOBAGO
TRINIDAD
VENEZUELA

Courtesy of Explorer Chart Books, www.explorercharts.com

Not to scale.

14

Ports of Entry

Abaco:
Government docks at Green Turtle Cay
Marsh Harbour
Sandy Point
Walkers Cay/ Grand Cay
Spanish Cay
Treasure Cay Marina

Andros:
Government docks at Congo Town
Fresh Creek
San Andros

Berry Islands:
Government dock at Great Harbour Cay
Great Harbour Cay Marina
Chub Cay Club Marina

Bimini:
Government dock at Brown's Marina
Sea Crest Marina
Bimini Big Game Club
Bimini Blue
Water Marina

Cat Cay:
Cat Cay Club Marina

Eleuthera:
Government docks at Governer's Harbour
North Eleuthera/ Harbour Island
Rock Sound
Spanish Wells

Exuma:
Government dock at George Town

Grand Bahama:
Docks at Freeport Bell Channel Marina
Port Lucaya Marina Village
Freeport Harbour
Running Mon Marina
Xanadu Marina
Government dock at West End

Great Inagua:
Government dock at Matthew Town

Long Island:
Stella Maris Marina

Mayaguana:
Government dock at Abraham's Bay

New Providence/ Nassau:
Arawak Cay
Bayshore Marina
Brown's Boat Basin
Clifton Pier
Coral Harbour Marina
East Bay Yacht Basin
Hurricane Hole Marina,
John Alfred Dock
Kelly's Dock
Lyford Cay Marina
Nassau Harbour Dock West
Union Dock

Ocean Cay:
Ocean Cay Dock

San Salvador:
Government dock at Cockburn Town

Turks & Caicos:
Providenciales
South Caicos

J. Raycroft

the Bahamas have been revered as one of the best vacationing spots in the world. With such a close proximity to the U.S., vacationing in paradise has never been easier.

Currency

The Bahamas use both the U.S. dollar and the Bahamian dollar. Since the Bahamian dollar is tied to the U.S. dollar, they are always relatively equal in rate. However, some of the outer islands are more likely to accept the Bahamian dollar due to the fact that it is the native currency. Credit cards (Visa, Mastercard and American Express) are accepted at most major establishments as well as Traveler's Checks. ATM's can also be found on the more populated islands such as Grand Bahama, New Providence Island (Nassau), the Abacos and others.

Customs and Immigration

Locations of Ports of Entry:

Abaco:	Government docks at Green Turtle Cay, Marsh Harbour, Sandy Point, Walkers Cay/ Grand Cay, Spanish Cay and the Treasure Cay Marina
Andros:	Government docks at Congo Town, Fresh Creek,San Andros
Berry Islands:	Government dock at Great Harbour Cay and Great Harbour Cay Marina; Chub Cay Club Marina
Bimini:	Government dock at Brown's Marina, Sea Crest Marina, Bimini Big Game Club, Bimini Blue Water Marina
Cat Cay:	Cat Cay Club Marina
Eleuthera:	Government docks at Governer's Harbour, North Eleuthera/ Harbour Island, Rock Sound, Spanish Wells
Exuma:	Government dock at George Town
Grand Bahama:	Docks at Freeport Bell Channel Marina, Port Lucaya Marina Village, Freeport Harbour, Running Mon Marina, Xanadu Marina, Government dock at West End
Great Inagua:	Government dock at Matthew Town
Long Island:	Stella Maris Marina
Mayaguana:	Government dock at Abraham's Bay
New Providence/ Nassau:	Arawak Cay, Bayshore Marina, Brown's Boat Basin, Clifton Pier, Coral Harbour Marina, East Bay Yacht Basin, Hurricane Hole Marina, John Alfred Dock, Kelly's Dock, Lyford Cay Marina, Nassau Harbour Dock West, Union Dock
Ocean Cay:	Ocean Cay Dock
San Salvador:	Government dock, Cockburn Town

Upon entering Bahamian waters, one must fly the yellow quarantine flag through clearance. There is a 24-hour grace period in which to clear. Clearance procedures are as follows; only the captain of the vessel is allowed ashore to clear in the vessel, accompanied with the ship's papers and each passenger's passport. There is a fee of $100 U.S. per boat entering the Bahamas for four or less persons. This fee includes a cruising permit, fishing permit, customs and immigration charges, plus $15 U.S. per person departure tax. Regular hours for Bahamas customs and immigration officers are 9am-5pm on weekdays, though officers are on-call after hours.

Airline Access

The following airlines service the Bahamas:

American Airlines	Continental Connection
American Eagle	Delta
Bahamasair	US Airways
TWA	Twin Air
Air Canada	British Airways
Chalk's International	

Communications

The calling system in the Bahamas is much like that of the U.S., with an area code of 242. For the Turks and Caicos, the area code is 946.

Calling the Bahamas from another country:
    from the U.S., dial 1 + 242 + 7-digit local number
    from the U.K., dial 00 + 1 +242 + the 7-digit local number.
Calling another country from the Bahamas:
    to the US, dial 1 + area code + 7-digit local number
    to another country, dial 011 + country code + area code and local number
Calling within an island:
    dial 7-digit local number
Calling island to island:
    dial 1 + 242 + 7-digit local number
Directory Assistance: 916
Operator (both local and international): 0
Internet Cafés:
    Cybercafé, Nassau: 242-394-6254
    Internet Café, Nassau: 242-356-2217

J. Raycroft

Cyber Club, Freeport: 242-351-4560
Radio Frequencies:
ZNS-1, 1540kHz: Principal Radio Station, 107.1 and 107.9
MHz: Nassau and Southeast Bahamas, ZNS-3, 810
kHz: Northern Bahamas, Grand Bahama, Abacos, Berry Islands, Biminis

Pay phones are available which take both Bahamian and US quarters, and there are also pay phones that accept phone cards that can be bought at BATELCO (Bahamas Telephone Co.).

Medical Facilities and Emergency Numbers

Abacos:
Marsh Harbour Government Clinic: 242-367-2510,
Green Turtle Cay Government Clinic: 242-365-4028
Police: 242-367-2560
Andros:
Government Clinics:
North Andros: 242-369-2055,
Central Andros: 242-368-2038
Police:
North Andros: 919
Central Andros: 242-368-2626
South Andros: 242-367-0083
Berry Islands:
Great Harbour Cay Medical Clinic: 242-367-8400
Police: 242-367-8344
Eleuthera:
Rock Sound Medical Clinic: 242-334-2226
Police: 242-334-2244
Governor Harbour's Medical Clinic: 242-332-2001
Police: 242-332-2111
The Harbour Island Health Centre: 242-333-2227
On-call doctor: 242-333-2822
Police: 919 or 242-333-2111
Exuma:
Government Medical Clinic in Georgetown:
242-336-2088
Police: 242-336-2666
Freeport/Lucaya:
Rand Memorial Hospital: 242-352-6735
Emergencies: 242-352-2689
Police: 911
Nassau:
Princess Margaret Hospital: 242-322-2861
Doctors Hospital: 242-322-8411
Police: 911, 919
Southern Bahamas:
San Salvador Medical Clinic: 242-331-2105
Police: 919, or 242-344-2599
Acklins Island and Crooked Island government operated clinics can be reached through front desk at hotels and the operator
Turks and Caicos:
Grand Turk Hospital: 649-946-2040
On Providenciales:
Providenciales Health Medical Center:
649-941-3000
Clinic on South Caicos: 649-946-3216
Middle Caicos: 649-946-6145

Sampson Cay, Bahamas   J. Raycroft

North Caicos: 649-946-7194
Police:
Grand Turk: 649-946-2299
Providenciales: 649-946-4259
South Caicos: 649-946-3299
North Caicos: 649-946-7261
Middle Caicos: 649-946-6111

For information on the Bahamas, may we suggest:

The Bahamas Cruising Guide by Mathew Wilson
Frommer's Bahamas 2002 by Darwin Porter and Danforth Prince
Cruising Guide to Abaco Bahamas by Steve, Jeff, and Jon Dodge
The Exuma Guide- A Guide to the Exuma Chain by Stephen Pavlidis
The Abaco Guide by Stephen Pavlidis
On and Off the Beaten Path by Stephen Pavlidis
Abaco Ports of Call by Tom Henschel

Bahamas Tourist Offices:
Head Office, Nassau: 242-356-4231/5216
Grand Bahama: 242-352-8356/8044
Eleuthera: 242-332-2142
Harbour Island: 242-333-2621
Abaco: 242-367-3067
Exuma: 242-336-2430
Bimini: 242-347-3529
Andros: 242-368-2286
South Andros: 242-369-1688
Turks and Caicos:
Grand Turk: 649-946-2321
Providenciales: 649-946-4970

Hopetown, Bahamas   J. Raycroft

Directory of Marinas & Services

Bahamas

Abaco Boat Harbour, Marsh Harbour, Abaco	242-367-2158
Abaco Yacht Services, Green Turtle Cay, Abacos	242-365-4033
Abaco Yacht Haven, Marsh Harbour, Abaco	242-367-3079
Admiral's Yacht Haven, Abaco	242-367-4242
Andros Lighthouse Yacht Club, Andros Island	242-368-2305
Bahama Bay Marina, Grand Bahama	242-352-4298
Bayshore Marina, New Providence	242-393-8232
Bell Channel Marina, Grand Bahama	242-373-2673
Bimini Beach Club Marina, Lake Worth, Bimini	954-257-0919
Bimini Big Game Fishing Club, Alice Town, North Bimini	242-347-3391
Bimini Bluewater Marina, Alice Town, North Bimini	242-347-3166
Bimini Sands, South Bimini	242-347-3500
Black Sound Marina, Green Turtle Cay, Abaco	242-365-4221
Bluff House Marina, Green Turtle Cay, Abaco	242-365-4247
Boat Harbour Marina, Marsh Harbour, Great Abaco	242-367-2736
Brown's Boat Basin, Nassau, New Providence	242-393-3331
Cape Eleuthera Marina, Eleuthera	242-334-8311
Captain Nemo's Marina, Nassau, New Providence	242-323-8426
Cat Cay Yacht Club, Cat Cay	242-347-3565
Chub Cay Club Marina, Chub Cay, Berry Islands	242-325-1490
Claridge Marina, South Nassau, New Providence	242-364-2218
Club Soleil Resort, Elbow Cay	242-366-0003
Conch Inn Marina, Marsh Harbour, Abaco	242-367-4000
Davis Harbour Marina, Eleuthera	242-334-6303
Deep Water Cay Club, Grand Bahama	407-687-3958

East Bay Yacht Basin, Nassau, New Providence	242-322-3754
Edwin's Boatyard, Abacos	242-365-6007
Exuma Docking Services, Georgetown, Exuma	242-336-2578
Exuma Fantasea, Exuma	242-336-3483
Farmer's Cay Yacht Club, Exuma	242-355-4017
Flamingo Bay Yacht Club and Marina, Freeport, Grand Bahama	888-311-7945
Flying Fish Marina, Long Island	242-337-3430
Fox Town Shell Service, Little Abaco	242-365-2046
Grand Cay Island Bay Front Hotel, Grand Cay, Abaco	242-359-4476
Green Turtle Yacht Club, Green Turtle, Abaco	242-365-4271
Great Harbour Cay Marina, Berry Islands	242-367-8838
Guana Marina, Guana Cay, Abaco	242-365-5133
Happy People Marina, Staniel Cay	242-355-2008
Harbour Island Club and Marina, Eleuthera	242-333-2427
Harbour View Marina, Marsh Harbour, Abaco	242-367-3810
Hatchet Bay Marina, Harbour Island, Eleuthera	937-835-5829
Hawks Nest Marina, Cat Island	242-357-7257
Highborne Cay Marina, Exuma	242-355-1008
Hope Town Hideaways Marina, Elbow Cay, Abacos	242-366-0224
Hope Town Marina, Elbow Cay, Abacos	242-366-0003
Hurricane Hole Marina, Nassau, New Providence	242-363-3600
Island Dreams, Treasure Cay, Abacos	242-365-8507
Lighthouse Marina, Hopetown, Elbow Cay, Abacos	242-366-0154
Lucayan Marina Village, Grand Bahama	242-373-7616
Lyford Cay Marina, Nassau, New Providence	242-362-4131
Mangoes Marina, Marsh Harbour, Abaco	242-367-4255

Man-O-War Marina, Man-O-War Cay, Abaco	242-365-6008
Marina at Atlantis, Paradise Island, New Providence	242-363-6068
Marine Service of Eleuthera, Hatchet Bay, Eleuthera	242-335-0186
Marsh Harbour Boatyard, Abaco	242-367-4011
Marsh Harbour Marina, Abaco	242-367-2700
Nassau Harbor Club, New Providence	242-393-0771
Nassau Yacht Haven Marina, New Providence	242-393-8173
Ocean Reef Yacht Club and Marina, Lucaya, Grand Bahama	242-373-4661
Old Bahama Bay Marina, Grand Bahama	242-346-6500
Orchid Bay Yacht Club and Marina, Great Guana Cay, Abacos	242-365-5175
Other Shore Club, Green Turtle Cay, Abaco	242-365-4197
Paradise Harbour Marina, Nassau, New Providence	242-363-2992
Point House, Spanish Cay, Abacos	242-359-6541
Port Lucaya Marina, Grand Bahama	242-373-9090
Port Of Call, Marsh Harbour, Abaco	242-367-2287
R & B Boatyard, Spanish Wells, Eleuthera	242-333-4462
Reflections Yacht and Beach Club, Rainbow Cay, Eleuthera	242-336-3483
Riding Rock Marina and Inn, Cockburn Town, San Salvador	954-359-8353
Running Mon Hotel and Marina, Freeport, Grand Bahama	242-352-6834
Sampson Cay Club and Marina, Exuma	242-355-2034
Sea Crest Hotel and Marina, Alice Town, North Bimini	242-347-3071

Sea Spray Resort Villas and Marina, Elbow Cay, Abacos	242-366-0065
Spanish Cay Marina, Spanish Cay, Abacos	242-365-0083
Spanish Wells Yacht Haven, St. George's Cay, Eleuthera	242-333-4255
Staniel Cay Yacht Club, Exuma	242-355-2011
Stella Maris Inn and Marina, Long Island	242-338-2055
Sumner Point Marina, Rum Cay	242-331-2823
Treasure Cay Marina, Abaco	242-365-8250
Valentine's Resort and Marina, Eleuthera	242-333-2142
Walkers Cay, Abaco (See our ad on p. 19)	242-352-1252
Weech's Bimini Dock, Alice Town, North Bimini	242-347-3028
Xanadu Marina, Freeport, Grand Bahama	242-352-6782

Turks and Caicos Islands

Caicos Marina and Shipyard, Providenciales	649-946-5600
Harbour Club Villas and Marina, Providenciales	649-941-5748
Leeward Marina, Providenciales	649-946-5674
Sea View Marina, South Caicos	649-946-3219

Directory of Boatyards & Services

Bahamas

Abaco Yacht Services, Green Turtle Cay, Abacos	242-365-4033
Brown's Boat Basin, Nassau, New Providence	242-393-3331
Edwin's Boatyard, Abacos	242-365-6007
Marsh Harbour Boatyard, Abaco	242-367-4011
R & B Boatyard, Spanish Wells, Eleuthera	242-333-4462

Turks and Caicos Islands

Caicos Marina and Shipyard, Providenciales	649-946-5600

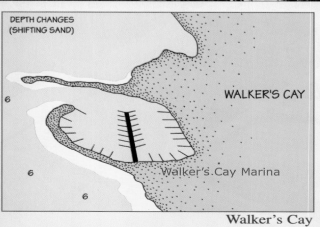

CUBA

The largest Eastern Caribbean Island,
Home to a Lively Latin Culture

Culture

Cuba has a long history of ownership and leadership. In the late 15th century, the Spanish, led by Christopher Columbus, began to take over the Arawak-inhabited island. The settlers began to produce such products as sugar cane and tobacco, both of which are still produced today, and African slaves were imported to the island. During the 17th century, European powers would struggle for the control of Cuba. However, Cuba didn't gain independence from the Spanish until 1899 when Spain gave control of Cuba to the United States with the signing of the Treaty of Paris. Cuba was granted independence in 1902 after four years of U.S. occupation, providing, via the Platt Amendment, that the U.S. could intervene with Cuban internal affairs when it came to U.S. interests on Cuba; however, the Platt Amendment would be abolished in 1933. In 1956, a young lawyer by the name of Fidel Castro, opposed the Batista regime through force and guerrilla tactics forcing Batista to renounce his office. In 1959, Fidel Castro became Cuba's leader. Castro would declare Cuba a socialist state in the 1961 and still remains in power now.

Cuba is saturated in culture. The island's influences are mainly Arawak Indian, African, Spanish and American. However, colonists from other countries have certainly added to the many flavors the island has to offer. Cuba is by far the largest island in the Greater Antilles with an area of approximately 50,000 square miles! Nevertheless, Cuba is yet an island country and is thus endowed with natural, island beauty such as beaches, palms, lush rain forest, mountains, fertile plains, tropical breezes and abundant wildlife. Because the island is so large, it is also metropolitan in some areas.

Havana, Cuba's capital, is legendary in terms of old colonial architecture.

Faded beauty abounds as cars from the 1950's, persuaded to continue operating through the ingenuity of their owners, peruse Havana's boulevards. Most of the old buildings are in disrepair - in need of some paint and polish.

New and modern European and Mexican hotel chains provide accommodations for European tourists soaking up the sun and sea, a scene in eerie contrast to the anachronistic beauty of the local way of life. Nevertheless, locals have for many years been considered very friendly and intelligent people, making visiting and vacationing quite an experience.

Currency

Although it is against the Trading with the Enemy Act, in conjunction with an economic embargo instated in 1961, for United States citizens to spend U.S. dollars in Cuba, the U.S. dollar is widely used along with the Cuban peso. The Cuban peso is officially tied to the U.S. dollar at par, but the market rate is closer to 20-25 pesos for 1 $U.S.

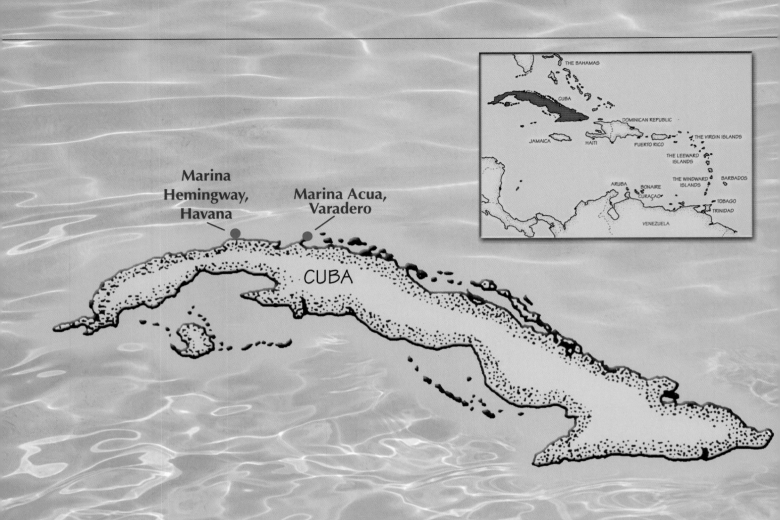

Marina
Hemingway,
Havana

Marina Acua,
Varadero

CUBA

THE BAHAMAS

CUBA

DOMINICAN REPUBLIC

THE VIRGIN ISLANDS

JAMAICA   HAITI   PUERTO RICO

THE LEEWARD
ISLANDS

ARUBA   BONAIRE   THE WINDWARD   BARBADOS
        CURAÇAO   ISLANDS

        TOBAGO
        TRINIDAD

VENEZUELA

Not to scale.

Havana, Cuba   W. Houghton, *The Diving Guide Cuba Scuba*

Marina Hemingway, Havana W. Houghton, *The Diving Guide Cuba Scuba*

Ports of Entry
Cuba:
Marina Hemingway, Havana
Marina Acua, Varadero

This small boy cradles his prized pet Jutia. Jutias are small mangrove critters that are hunted for their deliciously tender meat.

S. Charles, *Cruising Guide to Cuba*

Credit cards are widely accepted for all countries except those issued by U.S. banks and companies which are forbidden, as are checks and traveler's checks issued in the U.S.

Customs and Immigration

Around Cuba there exists a 12 nautical-mile territorial sea, and due to the rough measurement around the coast, the 12 miles can often extend to up to 20 miles. If you are leaving for Cuba from south of either West Palm Beach or Fort Myers, Florida, be sure to obtain a permit from the U.S. Coast Guard Marine Safety Office in Miami, FL (305-536-5691). Once inside the 12-mile limit, you must fly both the Cuban flag and the Q (quarantine) flag just beneath. There are two ports of entry on the northeastern section of Cuba that are strongly recommended. The first is Marina Hemingway, Havana, the second is Marina Acua, Varadero.

The following is necessary in order to clear in: clearance from your last port, ship's papers, and a crew list that includes the birth date, full name, passport number, issue date of passport, and position for each member aboard, a list of vessel, name, color, type, flag and port of registration, your last stop, intended entry-port in Cuba, estimated time of arrival and number of crew members. Remember: you must clear in and out with the Guarda Frontera (Cuban Coastal Defense Force) when moving the boat from one place to another, and always check with authorities ashore. Upon entering a new port, call "Seguridad Maritima" on VHF 16 to announce your arrival. If they don't respond, just pull up to the dock and wait for someone to arrive. Fees include the following: despacho (cruising permit), $25-$75 depending on length of vessel, additional fees, $35, departure fee, $10- $15.

Airline Access

There are quite a few commercial airlines that can be taken from the Caribbean, Europe, or Mexico to name a few, and many airlines that fly to numerous islands in the Caribbean. Thus, flying options aren't too limited, really. There are only a select few airlines in the U.S. that fly straight to Cuba, and they are charter planes. The following airlines fly into Cuba:

Air Jamaica	Air France
Iberia	Cubana
Martinair	Mexicana de Aviacion

Communications

Calling Cuba from another country:
    dial 011 + country code (53) + city or province code (listed below) + local number
Calling another country from Cuba:
    It is somewhat difficult to dial internationally. You can access a TELECORREO office or an international telephone center, or rent a cell phone from CUBACEL service (53-80-2222). CUBACEL can also assign a local number to a cell phone you bring. International calling cards are also available at local post offices and hotel desks. The U.S. cannot be dialed directly, so in that case it is better to use an ordinary phone and go through an operator. Email is another communication option.
Calling within Cuba:
    dial 0 + the city/province code + local number.
    Apparently, marinas are very willing to assist with local calls. Old pay phones take 5 centavo pieces, otherwise the new phones will take a 20 centavo coin and will han-

dle long distance as well. The following is a list of cities/provinces and their codes:

Baracoa 21	Bayamo 23
Camaguey 322	Cienfuegos 432
Guantánamo 21	Havana 7
Holguin 24	Isla de la Juventud 61
Las Tunas 31	Matanzas 52
Pinar del Rio 82	Sancti Spiritus 41
Santa Clara 422	Trinidad 419
Varadero 5	Viñales 8
Santiago de Cuba 226	

Directory Assistance: 113
Operator: 00
Internet Cafés:
    Cibercafe Capitolio, Havana: 53-7-669164
    Hotel Nacional, Havana: 53-7-333564
    El Colibri, Havana: 53-7-241360
    SuperClubs Puntarena, Varadero: 53-5-667125

Medical Facilities and Emergency Numbers

Ambulence, Havana: 7-404551-3, 7-405093/4
Fire, Havana: 7-811115
Police, Havana: 7-820116
Cardiovascular Emergency, Havana: 7-407173
International Clinics in Cuba:
    Centro Internacional Oftamologico "Camilo Cienfuefos", Havana, 7-325554
    Clinica Central "Cira Grarcia", 7-242811
    Clinica Internacional de Playas del Este, Havana, 7-971032
    Clinica Internacional de Varadero, Varadero, 5-667710

S. Charles, Cruising Guide to Cuba

Clinica Internacional de Cienfuegos,
     Cienfuegos, 432-451622
          Clinica Internacional de Trinidad, Trinidad, 419-3391
          Clinica Internacional de Cayo Coco,
          Ciego de Avila, 33-301205
          Clinica de Santa Lucia, Camaguey, 322-366203
          Clinica Internacional de Guardalavaca,
          Holguin, 24-30291
          Clinica Internacional Santiago de Cuba,
          Santiago de Cuba, 226-42589

For more information on Cuba, please refer to Simon Charles' **Cruising Guide to Cuba**. Contact Cruising Guide Publications at 800-330-9542 or www.cruisingguides.com.

Cuban Tourist Offices:
     Main Office: Ministerio de Turism de Cuba
     www.cubatravel.cu
Canada: Bureau de Tourisme de Cuba, 1 (514) 875-8004

Checking the boat's papers in Levisa, Cuba.

S. Charles, Cruising Guide to Cuba

Directory of Marinas & Services

Cuba

Marina Chapelín, Matanzas	53-45-66-7550
Marina Hemingway, Cuidad de La Habana	53-7-209-7270
Marina Internacional Puerto de Vita, Holguín	53-24-30-445
Marina Jagua, Cienfuegos	53-7-335-056
Marina Puertosol Cayo Coco-Guillermo, Ciego de Avila	53-33-30-1637
Marina Puertosol Cayo Largo del Sur, Isla de la Juventud	53-45-48-213
Marina Puertosol Cienfuegos, Cienfuegos	53-432-45-1241
Marina Puertosol Dársena de Varadero, Matanzas	53-45-66-8063
Marina Puertosol Tarará, Cuidad de La Habana	53-7-97-1462
Marina Puertosol Trinidad, Sancti Spiritus	53-419-6205
Marina Santiago de Cuba, Santiago de Cuba	53-226-691-446
Marina Varadero, Matanzas	53-45-66-7755

DOMINICAN REPUBLIC

J. Raycroft

J. Raycroft

Blessed with Superb Beaches, Mountains, and Gracious People

Culture

The country of the Dominican Republic is located on the island of Hispaniola, southeast of Cuba on the east side of the island. The country of Haiti occupies the west side. We have elected to leave Haiti out of this edition due to the conditions of political unrest, and are furthermore leaving open the option of inserting the country into later editions.

The isle of Hispaniola, though nearly half the size of Cuba, is still one of the largest in the Caribbean. The Dominican Republic, the larger half of Hispaniola, is 18,712 square miles of tropical beauty interwoven with urban settings. The country is home to eight million people of rather mixed decent. This heritage usually includes Indian, African and Latino. The culture of the Dominicans is derived from a rather complex past. In the early days of Hispaniola, as is the case with many of the Caribbean islands, Indians of the Arawak tribe were the only inhabitants. At the end of the 15th century, when Columbus landed on his first voyage to the West Indies, the Spanish began to settle, and eventually formed a colony in Santo Domingo, still the capital of the Dominican Republic today. Over the course of several centuries, the present-day Dominican Republic would also be colonized by Britain, France and, after 1821 when Haiti declared itself an independent country, Haiti.

The violence and contempt between the two countries would last consistently to present day. With economic failures, developing factions spurred by race and class distinction, coup attempts, and despot rulers, the U.S. finally decided to step in during the early 20th century, endeavoring to squelch civil unrest and political uncertainty. However, after the some eight years of occupation, the Dominican Republic's unrest was rekindled. Again more years of coups and civil wars ensued until 1966 when President Balaguer established a democracy that would last during his 30-year term. In 1996, President Reyna came into office for a four-year term, and in May of 2000, Hipolito Mejia was elected, the country having at least seemingly settled into democracy, standardized term lengths, and a formalized legislative system.

The Dominican Republic is a beautiful place to sail with both marinas and haul-out facilities available, not to mention incredible natural beauty and over 2,000 native species. The native language is Spanish; English is rarely spoken.

Currency

The currency in the Dominican Republic is the Dominican peso (RD$). Many stores and restaurants in the DR accept both U.S. dollars and the Dominican peso. The exchange rate is best if done in the country itself. Credit cards, travelers checks and ATM's are available.

Customs and Immigration

The following are the reported Ports of Entry for the Dominican Republic:

Luperón,
Puerto Blanco

Pepillo Salcedo,
Manzanillo Bay

Puerto Plata

Samaná

DOMINICAN
REPUBLIC

Punta

Santo
Domingo

La Romana

San Pedro
de Macoris

Bajos de Haina

Not to scale.

Ports of Entry

North Coast:
Pepillo Salcedo, Manzanillo Bay
Luperón, Puerto Blanco
Puerto Plata
Samaná
Punta Cana

South Coast:
La Romana
San Pedro de Macoris
Santo Domingo
Bajos de Haina

J. Raycroft

Fly the yellow quarantine flag upon approaching a Port of Entry in the Dominican Republic. As it is illegal to go ashore before clearance, wait for officials. The following are required for clearance into the country: clearance from the last port of call, passports for all crew, and the ship's documents. Those without Visas already must purchase a tourist card, good for two months and renewable. Some Ports of Entry have harbor fees.

*Please check with Dominican Republic officials before going, as regulations might have changed.

Airline Access

There are many airlines to fly in order to get to the Dominican Republic, and many ways in which you can fly. These are just a few of the many airlines that either have direct or indirect access to the DR.

Aeromar	Air Europa
Air France	Air Santo Domingo
American Airlines	American Eagle
Caribair	Continental
Copa	Costuristica
Cubana	General Airlines
Iberia	LIAT
Northwest	TWA
US Airways	

Communications

Dominican Republic phone numbers are similar to those in the U.S. with an area code of 809.

Calling the DR from another country:
    from the U.S., dial 1 + 809 + 7-digit local number
    from the U.K., dial 00 + 809 + 7-digit local number
Calling another country from the DR:
    to the U.S., dial 1 + area code + 7-digit local number
    to the U.K., dial 011 + 44 + city code and local number
Calling within the DR:
    dial only local 7-digit number
Operator: 0
Directory Enquiries: 411

In the Dominican Republic long distance is the cheapest of all the Caribbean. Phone booths are available to call collect. The phone system is serviced by CODETEL, and you can make calls from their offices. They also have internet access.

Internet Cafés:
    Café Internet/Cybercafé,
    Santo Domingo, 809-562-6245
    Cyber Colomado, Boca Chica, 809-523-4282
    Hot.com Café, Puerto Plata, 809-342-5500
    Internet Café, Cyber Café, Santo Domingo,
    809-685-3777
    MP Coffee-net, Santo Domingo, 809-686-1919
    Playa Dorado NetWork, Puerto Plata, 809-320-2256
    Punto Internet Luperon, 809-571-8469
    RIU Internet Café, Puerto Plata, 809-320-4000
        ext.1869
    Sam's Bar and Grill, Puerto Plata, 809-586-7267
    Teledominicana, Santo Domingo, 809-537-6544

Medical Facilities and Emergency Numbers

Fire/Ambulance/Police: 911
Centro Cardiovascular, Santo Domingo: 809-682-6071
Hospital Jose Maria Cabral, Santiago: 809-583-4311
Centro Médico Oriental: 809-586-2210
Red Cross Ambulance Services,
Santo Domingo: 809-689-4288
Servicio de Ambulancias 24 Horas: 809-530-8221

For more information on the Dominican Republic, please refer to Bruce Van Sant's *A Gentleman's Guide to Passages South*.

Tourist Office:
    Santo Domingo, 809-685-9054, 809-685-5254

Directory of Marinas & Services

Dominican Republic

Best Western Metro Hotel Marina, Juan Dolio	809-526-2811
Cap Cana, Punta Cana	coming soon
Casa De Campo, La Romana	809-523-3333
Marina Punta Cana, Santo Domingo	809-221-2262

J. Raycroft

J. Raycroft

J. Raycroft

PUERTO RICO

From Rainforests to Sunny Beaches to Casinos and Salsa, Puerto Rico is a Dynamic Destination

Culture

Puerto Rico is a 3,500 square-mile island about 1,000 miles southeast of Miami. Her population is no less than 3.9 million. Puerto Rico and the Spanish Virgin Islands' history is a rich blend of Taino, Spanish, African, and American. Her population consisted entirely of Taino Indians until the late 15th century when Spaniard Christopher Columbus came to colonize the West Indies. The Spanish began to colonize Puerto Rico in hopes of finding gold in this 'rich port.' In the early 16th century, laws were passed to keep the Taino's in wage-free forced labor, and later replaced with laws to pay wages for labor and to teach the Taino's Christianity. However, these laws did very little, for the Taino's remained close to slavery for many years. It wasn't until 1514 that a law was passed to allow the Spaniards on the island to marry the Taino. This, coupled with the importation of African slaves in 1521, began the cultural diversity that would later blossom into modern day Puerto Rico's no-race-discrimination ideology and way of life. Puerto Rico remained a Spanish colony until 1898, the year that concluded the Spanish-American War with the ceding of Cuba, Puerto Rico and the other Spanish owned islands to the U.S. In 1952, Puerto Rico officially became the Commonwealth of Puerto Rico including Vieques and Culebra, under which Puerto Ricans would now have U.S. passports and would be able to move and live freely between the U.S. and Puerto Rico.

As is true for many of the islands in the Caribbean, many of the remnants of Spanish colonialism are present in architecture, culture, and way of life. Puerto Rico is rich with history and diversity and for this reason is a pleasure to visit. Geographically, Puerto Rico is mountainous with its highest peak, Cerro de Punta, reaching a height of nearly 4,400 feet. The land contains many lush forests and fertile valleys on which is grown sugar, coffee, and fruits such as pineapples, plantains, and bananas. Whilst there was once a large tobacco producing industry, there is now instead a rising dairy industry on the island. Nevertheless, Puerto Rico remains tropical with beaches, palms, city life and isolation, and a Latin flare and vigor that brings it all together.

Both English and Spanish are spoken on Puerto Rico and the Spanish Virgin Islands.

Currency

Since Puerto Rico is a commonwealth of the United States, the currency used is the U.S. dollar. Credit cards, and Traveler's checks are widely accepted, and ATM's are available.

Customs and Immigration

U.S. vessels returning from foreign waters including the U.S. Virgin Islands should purchase an annual customs user's decal ($25) before arriving to Puerto Rico.

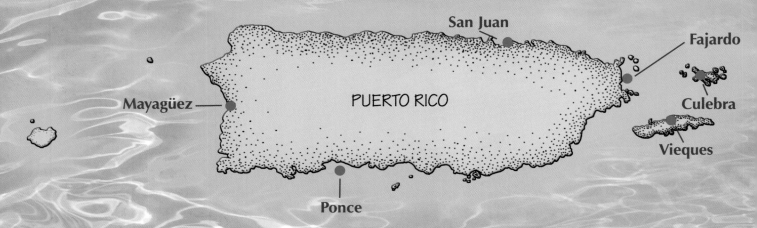

San Juan

Fajardo

Mayagüez

PUERTO RICO

Culebra

Vieques

Ponce

Not to scale.

Ports of Entry

Puerto Rico:
Mayagüez
Ponce
Fajardo
San Juan
Vieques
Culebra

J. Raycroft

Ports of entry are as follows:

Mayagüez (787-831-3342)   Ponce (787-841-3130)
Fajardo (787-863-0950)   San Juan (787-253-4533)
On Vieques: (787-741-8366)   On Culebra: (787-742-3531)

Customs and Immigration hours are 8am-5pm, Monday through Friday. On off-hours, weekends and holidays, report to the San Juan port of entry via phone. U.S. vessels with U.S. crew may be able to clear in entirely by phone.

Airline Access

The following is a list of some of the airlines that fly to and from Puerto Rico, however there are many more.

Air Caraibes	Air Guadeloupe
American Airlines	American Eagle
American Trans Air	British Airways
Cape Air	Delta Airlines
Iberia	Liat
Northwest Airlines	TWA
United Airlines	US Air

Communications

Puerto Rico's phone system is the same as that of the U.S. with an area code of 787. The area code is the same for Vieques and Culebra, however, the first three digits for the local 7-digit number remain the same:

for Vieques, 787-741 + the 4-digit local number, for Culebra, 787-742 + 4-digit local number.

Calling Puerto Rico from another country:
from the U.S., dial 1 + 787 + the local 7-digit number, from the U.K., dial 00 + 1 + 787 and 7-digit local number

Calling another country from Puerto Rico:
to the U.S., dial 1 + the area code and 7-digit local number
to the U.K. dial 011 + 44 + plus the city code and local number

Calling within Puerto Rico: dial all 10 digits.
Directory Assistance: 411
Operator: 0

Pay phones are available, some of which are coin-operated and others that take phone cards that can be bought in drugstores and gift shops.

Internet Cafés:
Cybernet Café, Isla Verde, 787-728-4195
Soapy's Station, Old San Juan, 787-289-0344
Computadoras Por Hora @ Internet Café,
San Juan, 787-751-1232
CyberNet Puerto Rico, Condado, 787-724-4033
CyberNet Café @ Isla Verde, San Juan, 787-791-3138
Cyberw@rks, Rio Piedras, 787-766-2134
Calling Station & Internet Café,
San Juan, 787-977-2182
Peek a Boo, Fajardo, 787-863-6828
Password Café, San German, 787-892-4485

Medical Facilities and Emergency Numbers

Air Ambulance: 787-756-3424
Centro Medico Rio Piedras Air Ambulance: 787-754-3535
Fire Department: 787-343-2330

Life Threatening Emergency: 911
Medical Emergencies: 787-343-2550, 754-2550
Police Department: 787-343-2020
Coast Guard: 787-729-6770

Hospitals:
Bayamon Municipal Hospital: 787-740-5226
Carolina Municipal Hospital: 787-757-1800
San Juan Municipal Hospital: 787-766-2222

For Vieques:
Police: 787-741-2020
Fire: 787-741-2111
Hospital: 787-741-2151
Towing: 787-741-2462

For Culebra:
Police: 787-742-3501/0106
Fire: 787-742-3530
Hospital: 787-742-3511

For more information on Puerto Rico and the Spanish Virgin Islands, please refer to Bruce Van Sant's Guide to the Spanish Virgin Islands, the back of Nancy and Simon Scott's *Cruising Guide to the Virgin Islands*, page 246 of the 11th edition. Contact Cruising Guide Publications at 800-330-9542 or www.cruisingguides.com.

Puerto Rico Tourist Office:
    Department of Tourism, San Juan, 800-866-7827

Directory of Marinas & Services
Puerto Rico

Club Deportivo de Oeste	787-851-8880
Club Nautico de Arecibo	787-878-8465
Club Nautico de Boqueron	787-851-1336
Club Nautico de Guayama	787-866-3162
Club Nautico de La Parguera	787-899-5590
Club Nautico de Rincon	787-823-8800
Club Nautico de San Juan	787-722-0190
Club Nautico de Vega Baja	787-858-7656
Isleta Marina, Fajardo	787-643-2180
Marina De Salinas	787-752-8484
Marina Puerto Real, Fajardo	787-863-2188
Palmas Del Mar, Humacao	787-852-6000
Ponce Yacht and Fishing Club, Ponce	787-842-9003
Puerto Chico, Fajardo	787-863-0834
Puerto Del Ray Marina, Fajardo	787-860-1000
San Juan Bay Marina *(See our ad on p. 38)*	787-721-8062
Sea Lovers Marina, Fajardo	787-860-1000
Villa Marina Yacht Harbour, Fajardo	787-863-5131
Wyndham El Conquistador Marina, Fajardo	787-863-6594

Directory of Boatyards & Services
Puerto Rico

Isleta Marina, Fajardo	787-643-2180
Marina De Salinas	787-752-8484
Ponce Yacht and Fishing Club, Ponce	787-842-9003
Puerto Del Ray Marina, Fajardo	787-860-1000
San Juan Bay Marina *(See our ad on p. 38)*	787-721-8062
Villa Marina Yacht Harbour, Fajardo	787-863-5131

J. Raycroft

A. Blake

VIRGIN ISLANDS

Consistent Trade Winds and Numerous Protected Anchorages Makes this a Sailor's Paradise

Culture

The Virgin Islands are considered by some to be among the best sailing waters in the world. Positioned at the top of the Caribbean island chain, the Virgins have had a very long and disputed history of ownership. According to some of the earliest recorded information, the population of the islands consisted of a very peaceful tribe of Indians called the Arawaks. It is said however that this tribe was succeeded by a more aggressive crew called the Caribs who were eventually eradicated by the Spanish in the 16th century. Though Columbus discovered these islands during several successive trips to the Caribbean in the early 1490's, the Virgins (named historically for St. Ursula and her 11,000 virgins) were for centuries a kind of open port in which many pirates and bucca-neers could conduct illegal activities and live comfortably on their spoils on the small scattered islands that had yet to be colonized by law and religion. In this time Denmark owned and had colonized St. Thomas and St. John. In 1672, the British took possession of Tortola by way of a kind of influx of colonists from the already British-established 'Colony of the Leeward Islands', and by the same means later took the rest of the B.V.I. Almost a century later, Denmark bought St. Croix from France, which would give them ownership over all of the US Virgins. It wasn't until 1917 that, realizing that the now US Virgins had a militarily advantageous position, the US finally bought them for 25 million dollars.

Now, the Virgins are a sailing haven. The Virgin Islands are unique because of their proximity to each other, which allows for fabulous day sails from one stunning anchorage to another. The Virgins in this approximately 30-square mile area consist of two groups: the US Virgins Islands and the British Virgin Islands. Each group has its individual charm and character. That being said, they have many things in common including a very laid back personality and a beauty that hasn't surrendered to an increasing population and tourist interest.

The Virgin Islands, home to very calm and easily navigated seas that are famously vibrant and clear, have for many years been extremely boat-friendly. In fact, it could be said that many of its beauties can only be found by sea, which, over the years has given way to quite a solid peppering of boats all over the Virgins. Though there are over 50 islands that make up the Virgins, most of the 50 are uninhabited. The major ones that are settled include Tortola, Virgin Gorda, Jost Van Dyke, Anegada and Peter Island (which is inhabited only so far as a resort and a couple houses) in the British Virgins and St. John, St. Croix, and St. Thomas in the US Virgins. Much of the charm of the islands consists in the ability to float (or sail) peacefully in and out of habitation. No matter where you are, though, on any clear night you can always count on seeing the Milky Way.

Currency

The Virgin Islands officially use U.S. currency, and accept most major credit cards and also traveler's checks. There are also a few ATMs to be found in both parts of the Virgins.

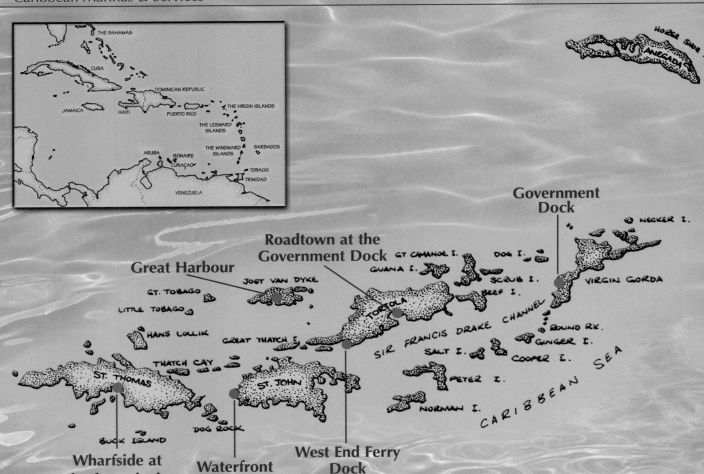

Government Dock

Roadtown at the Government Dock

Great Harbour

THE BAHAMAS

CUBA

DOMINICAN REPUBLIC

JAMAICA HAITI PUERTO RICO THE VIRGIN ISLANDS

THE LEEWARD ISLANDS

THE WINDWARD ISLANDS BARBADOS

ARUBA BONAIRE CURAÇAO

TOBAGO TRINIDAD

VENEZUELA

HORSE SHOE REEF

ANEGADA

NECKER I.

GT CAMANOE I. DOG I.

GUANA I. SCRUB I.

JOST VAN DYKE BEEF I. VIRGIN GORDA

GT. TOBAGO TORTOLA

LITTLE TOBAGO ROUND RK.

HANS LOLLIK GREAT THATCH I. SIR FRANCIS DRAKE CHANNEL GINGER I.

THATCH CAY SALT I. COOPER I.

ST. THOMAS GREAT THATCH PETER I.

ST. JOHN NORMAN I. CARIBBEAN SEA

DOG ROCK

BUCK ISLAND

Wharfside at the ferry dock, Charlotte Amalie

Waterfront at Cruz Bay

West End Ferry Dock

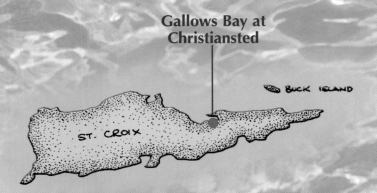

Gallows Bay at Christiansted

BUCK ISLAND

ST. CROIX

Not to scale.

Ports of Entry

United States Virgin Islands:
Wharfside at the ferry dock, Charlotte Amalie, St. Thomas
Waterfront at Cruz Bay, St. John
Gallows Bay at Christiansted, St. Croix

British Virgin Islands:
Roadtown at the Government Dock, Tortola
West End Ferry Dock, Tortola
Government Dock, Virgin Gorda
Great Harbour, Jost Van Dyke

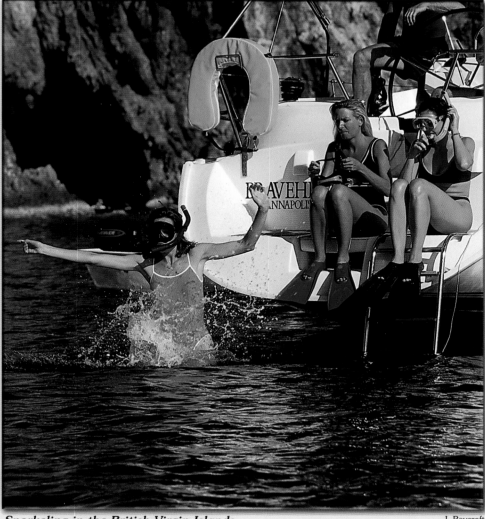

Snorkeling in the British Virgin Islands

J. Raycroft

Customs and Immigration

It will be necessary to clear customs and immigration when going from the US Virgins to the British Virgins or vice versa. You must also clear your vessel in the original territory before proceeding to the nearest port of call in the other. The locations of the ports of entry are as follows:

St. Thomas: Wharfside at the ferry dock, Charlotte Amalie
St. John: Waterfront at Cruz Bay
St. Croix: Gallows Bay at Christiansted
Tortola: Roadtown at the Government Dock
                 West End ferry dock
Virgin Gorda: Airport or Government Dock
Jost Van Dyke: Great Harbour

Regular hours for British Customs are from 8:30-4:30, Monday through Friday, and 8:30-12:30 on Saturdays. Outside these hours, raise your quarantine flag and clear at the first available opportunity. Hours for U.S. Customs are 8am-12pm, and 1pm-5pm, Monday through Sunday, however, overtime charges will be incurred on Sundays. Fees range from eight to ten dollars depending on the day and size of the vessel.

S. Scott

Airline Access

The following airlines service the British Virgin Islands:

Clair Aero Services	LIAT
American Eagle	Air Sunshine
Cape Air	Air St. Thomas
Caribbean Star	Fly BVI (charter)
Island Helicopters International (charter)	

The following airlines service the U.S. Virgin Islands:

Air St. Thomas	American Airlines
American Eagle	Delta Airlines
Seaborne Aviation Inc.	TWA
US Airways	LIAT
Air Sunshine	Cape Air
Continental	Northwest
Gulfstream International Airways	United
Bohlke International Airways (charter)	

Communications

The calling system for the Virgin islands is like that of the U.S. with an area code of 284 for the British Virgins, and 340 for the U.S. Virgins.

Calling the Virgin Islands from another country:
   from the U.S., dial 1 + area code (284 or 340) + 7-digit local number
   from the U.K., dial 001 + area code (284 or 340) + the 7-digit local number
Calling another country from the Virgin Islands:
   to the U.S., dial 1 + area code + 7-digit local number
   to the U.K., dial 011 + country code + area code and local number
Calling within the USVI: dial 7-digit local number
Calling within the BVI: dial 7-digit local number
Calling between the USVI and the BVI: dial 1 + area code + 7-digit local number
Directory Assistance: for BVI, dial 119 local and 110 for international for USVI, dial 913
Operator (for both USVI and BVI): 0 for local calls, 00 for international calls

Several USA Direct Dial telephones are available throughout the islands as well as coin and telephone card phones.

Internet Cafés: Soapy's Station, St. Thomas, 340-776-7170
   Phone Card Center: St. Thomas, 340-774-8466
   Beans, Bytes, & Websites, St. Thomas, 340-777-7089
   Strand Street Station, St. Croix, 340-719-6245
   Cyber Café at Caribbean Printing Co., Tortola 284-494-2413
   Myett's Restaurant, Tortola, 284-495-9543
   Trellis Bay Cyber Café, Tortola, 284-495-2447
   Caribbean Jewelers Cyber Café, Tortola, 284-495-4137

Medical Facilities and Emergency Numbers

BVI	USVI
Police: 999	Police: 911
Fire: 999	Fire: 911
Ambulance: 999	Ambulance: 911
Hospital: 494-3497	

VISAR (Virgin Islands Search and Rescue): 284-494-4357/494-6613 or 767 (SOS)

For more information of the Virgin Islands, please refer to Nancy and Simon Scott's **Cruising Guide to the Virgin Islands**, 11th edition. Contact Cruising Guide Publications at 800-330-9542 or www.cruisingguides.com.

Virgin Islands Tourist Offices:
   BVI Tourist Board, Road Town, Tortola: 284-494-3134
   USVI Dept. of Tourism, St. Thomas: 340-774-8784

Directory of Marinas & Services

United States Virgin Islands: St. Thomas

Saga Haven Marina, Benner Bay	340-775-9671
Independent Boatyard and Marina, **Benner Bay** *(See our ad on p. 45)*	340-776-0466
La Vida Marina, Benner Bay	340-775-6901
Fish Hawk Marina, Benner Bay	340-775-9058
Crown Bay Marina	340-774-2255
Yacht Haven Marina, **Charlotte Amalie** *(See our ad on p. 45)*	340-774-6050
Compass Point Marina, Benner Bay	340-775-6144
Tropical Marina/Ruan's, Benner Bay	340-775-6595
American Yacht Harbour, Red Hook	340-775-6454
Sapphire Beach Resort and Marina, East End	340-775-6100
Vessup Point Marina, Red Hook	340-775-9964

United States Virgin Islands: St. Croix

Green Cay Marina	340-773-1453
Salt River Marina	340-778-9650
St. Croix Marine, Christiansted	340-773-0289
St. Croix Yacht Club Marina, Teague Bay	340-773-9531

United States Virgin Islands: St. John

Caneel Bay Shipyard	340-693-8771

Directory of Boatyards & Services

United States Virgin Islands: St. Thomas

Haulover Marine, Sub Base	340-776-2078
Independent Boatyard and Marina, **Benner Bay** *(See our ad on p. 45)*	340-776-0466

United States Virgin Islands: St. Croix

St. Croix Marine, Christiansted	340-773-0289

J. Raycroft

Directory of Marinas & Services

British Virgin Islands: Tortola
MegaServices Marina, Baughers Bay, Road Town   284-494-1459
Soper's Hole Wharf and Marina, West End
(See our ad on p. 54)   284-495-4589
Frenchman's Cay Shipyard and Marina,
West End *(See our ad on p. 52)*   284-495-4353
Fort Burt Marina, Road Town   284-494-4200
Prospect Reef Resort and Marina, Road Town   284-494-3311
Road Reef Marina, Road Town   284-494-2751
Village Cay Marina, Road Town   284-494-2771
The Moorings at Wickhams Cay, Road Town   284-494-2331
Inner Harbour Marina, Road Town   284-494-4502
Marina Cay Resort   284-494-2174
Peter Island Resort and Yacht Harbour   284-495-2000
Footloose Dock, Road Town   284-494-0529
Tortola Yacht Services, Road Town
(See our ad on p. 46)   284-494-2124
Hodges Creek Marina, Maya Cove   284-494-5538
Tropic Island Yacht Management, Maya Cove   284-494-2450
Nanny Cay Marina and Boatyard
(See our ad on p. 47, 48)   284-494-2512
Harbourview Marina, East End   284-495-1775
BVI Yacht Club, Road Town   284-494-3286
Penn's Landing Marina, East End   284-495-1134

British Virgin Islands: Virgin Gorda
Yacht Harbour, The Valley   284-495-5500
Bitter End Yacht Club, North Sound   284-494-2746

S. Scott

| Road Harbour | Tortola | British Virgin Islands |

☑ Radio channel monitored: 16
☑ Boat accommodation: Up to 20 foot beam, 9.5 foot draft and 70 tons
☑ Haul-out equipment/machinery: Marine travelifts 40 and 70 tons
☐ Haul-out fee:
☑ Time alotted for haul-out: As required
☑ Mechanic on premises: Yes
☑ Yard only work: Yes
☑ Do-it-yourself work: Yes
☑ Customer supplied paints/parts allowed: Yes
☑ Yard specialites: Awlgrip, stainless steel fabrication, fiberglass repairs, shipwright, diesel, outboard sales & services

☐ Fuel:
☐ Water:
☑ Chandlery on premises: Yes
☑ Hours: Monday - Friday 7:00am - 5:00pm 24 hour emergencies
☑ Currency/Credt Cards accepted: All cards accepted and US dollar
☐ Associated marina: n/a
☑ Associated repair facilities: All marine repair services within easy walking distance
☐ Provisions:
☐ Other yard services:

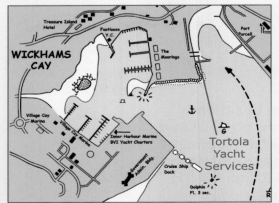

Wickham's Cay, Road Harbour

Tortola Yacht Services
Wickham's Cay, Road Harbour
Tortola, British Virgin Islands

Phone 284-494-2124 • Fax 284-494-4707
tys@tysbvi.com • www.tysbvi.com

Saba Rock Resort, North Sound   284-495-9966
Leverick Bay Resort and Marina, North Sound   284-495-7421

Directory of Boatyards & Services

British Virgin Islands: Tortola
**Frenchman's Cay Shipyard and Marina,
West End** *(See our ad on p. 52)*   284-495-4353
Tortola Yacht Services, Road Town
(See our ad on p. 46)   284-494-2124
Nanny Cay Marina and Boatyard
(See our ad on p. 47, 48)   284-494-2512

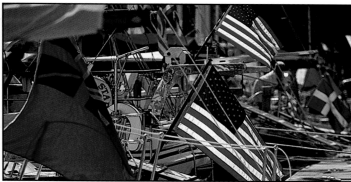

J. Raycroft

| Nanny Cay | Tortola | British Virgin Islands |

- ☑ Radio channel monitored: 16, 68
- ☑ Transient dockage: Yes
- ☑ Longterm dockage: Yes
- ☐ Anchoring near marina: No
- ☐ Dockage rate:
- ☐ Mooring rate:
- ☐ Longest length: 140ft
- ☑ Catamaran dockage: Yes
- ☐ Depth at low water:
- ☑ Electricity: Yes
- ☑ Water: Yes
- ☑ Fuel: Yes
- ☐ Pump out station:
- ☑ Showers: Yes
- ☑ Ice: Yes
- ☐ Telephone hook-up: No
- ☐ TV/cable: No
- ☑ Chandlery: Yes
- ☐ Customs/Immigration: No
- ☑ Hours: 8:00am-6:30 Daily
- ☐ Currency/Credit Cards accepted:
- ☑ Provisions: Full service
- ☑ Restaurant(s): Yes
- ☑ Bars: Yes
- ☑ Computer access: Coconut Telegraph
- ☑ Marine Services: Haulout facilities, full service boatyard for storage & repairs, refinishing, rigging, 40 room hotel (20% Off for marina guests), swimming pool, tennis court, volley ball court

Nanny Cay, Tortola

J. Raycroft

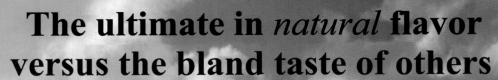

TORTOLA

Soper's Hole, Tortola

- ☑ Radio channel monitored: 16
- ☑ Transient dockage: 24 slips
- ☐ Longterm dockage: n/a
- ☑ Anchoring near marina: No
- ☑ Dockage rate: $1.25/ft/day
- ☑ Mooring rate: $20/day
- ☑ Longest length: 150ft
- ☑ Catamaran dockage: Yes
- ☑ Depth at low water: 36ft
- ☑ Electricity: Yes
- ☑ Water: Yes
- ☑ Fuel: Yes
- ☑ Pump out station: No
- ☑ Showers: Yes
- ☑ Ice: Yes
- ☐ Telephone hook-up: No

- ☐ TV/cable: No
- ☐ Chandlery: No
- ☑ Customs/Immigration: Yes
- ☑ Hours: 8:00am - 6:00pm
- ☑ Currency/Credit Cards accepted: U.S. Dollar, Visa, MasterCard
- ☑ Provisions: Yes
- ☑ Restaurant(s): Yes
- ☑ Bars: Yes
- ☑ Computer access: Yes
- ☑ Marine Services: Alongside Shipyard

Soper's Hole Marina, situated in the beautiful West End of Torotola, with it's crystal clear water and breezy anchorages is a must for every boating enthusiast. Watch the magical, spectacular sunsets from this charming bay whilst enjoying an evening cocktail in the tropical breeze.

A warm and friendly welcome from all our staff at the marina awaits those who visit this piece of paradise.

Soper's Hole Marina is a deep draft marina that can accommodate yachts/catamarans up to 36ft draft with short and long term dockage for up to 24 yachts. Fuel, water, electricity and hot showers are all part of the facilitites that the marina offers. There are also 18 overnight moorings available in the bay.

Four tastefully furnished and air-conditioned rooms with bay views, cable TV, fridges and telephone make the perfect overnight place to stay.

Full shore side facilities are available, including good eating retaurants, lively bars that offer Caribbean entertainment during the season, and a choice of shops that sell unique tropical clothing and Caribbean design gifts. Full gourmet style provisioning offers all sorts of tasty delights that will tantalize any palette.

If you are a keen diver be assured that you now have an award winning dive operator located in this marina to see to your every diving requirement.

All of us here at Soper's Hole Marina look forward to welcoming you in the future and in making your vacation stopover one you will always remember.

VOYAGE

Soper's Hole Marina
Frenchman's Cay, Tortola
British Virgin Islands

Phone 284-474-0740 • Fax 284-474-0741
VHF Channel 16
cathy@voyagecharters.com • www.multihullmarina.com

Fat Cat
CHARDONNAY

or

Sour Puss
GISBORNE SEMILLON

...New Zealand wines imported by TICO from Coopers Creek, Haupai.

Select wines from Australia, California,
Chile, France, Italy, South Africa, Spain &...Premium spirits,
Cuban cigars, beers, waters & juices.

www.ticobvi.com

TICO is three minutes from the Moorings, Road Town.
Order in advance to have your order ready on your arrival,
or take advantage of our **FREE DELIVERY** service.

Penfolds
Australia's Most Famous Wine

GEORGES DUBŒUF

Marqués de Cáceres
RIOJA

Chalone
Wine Group

(284) 494-2211 • Fax: (284) 494-4888 • Email: tico@surfbvi.com
Monday / Friday 9:00 am - 6:00 pm • Saturday 9:00 am - 3:00 pm

55

LEEWARD
ISLANDS

Gustavia St. Barts

Diverse Cultures, Rich History and Different Island Landscapes

The Leewards consist largely of about 12 islands spread out over 200 miles of Caribbean Sea. The islands are so diverse, that really just traveling through them affords one a melange of different climates and personalities to visit. Largely volcanic in origin, the Leewards form a line of islands stringing from the top of the West Indies island chain beginning at the Virgin Islands to Dominica at its bottom including Anguilla, St. Martin/Sint Maarten, St. Barts, Saba, Statia, St. Kitts, Nevis, Montserrat, Antigua, Barbuda, Guadeloupe and the Saintes, and finally Dominica. Ten of these islands are independent island nations.

The Leeward Islands are both historically and culturally diverse, and thus more than just mere traces of French, English, and Dutch colonialism can be found here. In fact, the marrying of old colonial architecture and customs with the backdrop of paradisic surroundings, island laissez-faire and those ever-present balmy breezes makes for quite a breathtaking destination. The tip-tops of the islands can be rugged mountains with peaks jutting up from the green interior, sloping green hills or sandy dunes. The hearts of some of the islands contain tropical rainforests in which waterfalls empty into pools and rivers that finally flow into the sea. Natural springs can also be found in the Leewards, one of which, located in Dominica, has been known for centuries to bring health to the ailing and longevity to the aging. Due to the distance between islands and lack of as many natural harbors and anchorages, the Leeward Islands are still a true discovery for those who journey by sea.

St. Martin

Culture

St. Martin is divided into two sides, the French side and the Dutch side. Each side has its own capital, the French capital is Marigot, the Dutch is Philipsburg. Originally (circa the 17th century) the salt trade was a Spanish crown endeavor. Though St. Martin was never a possession or settlement for Spain, still it was important to keep a Spanish garrison in order that the island's salt pans didn't become a source for black market salt. Eventually, the garrison was reassigned, and the fort was dismantled in 1648. The settlements that did inhabit the island included the Dutch and the French. In 1648 a treaty was signed stating that each owned a half of the island and that failure to recognize this or the mistreating of a person or persons on the other side would be treated as a war crime and dealt with accordingly. To this day, centuries of old architecture is evident as you walk the streets of the small towns that still exist on the island.

The languages spoken on the island are as follows: French is primarily spoken on the French side though English is widely understood, and Dutch and English are spoken on the Dutch side.

Currency

Though the US dollar is universally accepted on both sides of the island, prices are often quoted in Euros on the French side

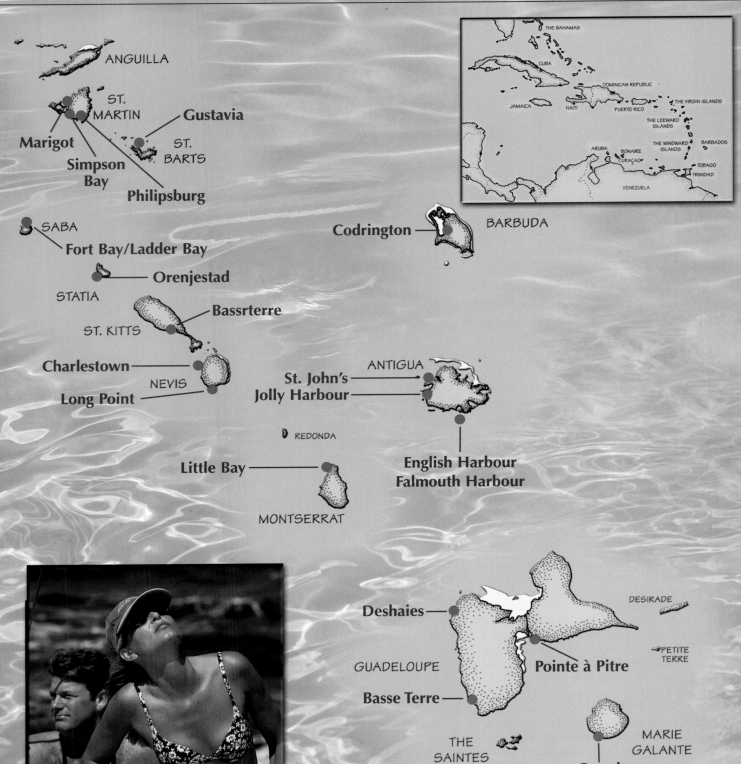

ANGUILLA

ST. MARTIN

Gustavia

Marigot

ST. BARTS

Simpson Bay

Philipsburg

SABA

Fort Bay/Ladder Bay

Codrington — BARBUDA

Orenjestad

STATIA

Bassrterre

ST. KITTS

Charlestown

NEVIS

Long Point

St. John's — ANTIGUA

Jolly Harbour

REDONDA

Little Bay

English Harbour
Falmouth Harbour

MONTSERRAT

DESIRADE

Deshaies

PETITE TERRE

GUADELOUPE

Pointe à Pitre

Basse Terre

MARIE GALANTE

THE SAINTES

Grand Bourg

Portsmouth

DOMINICA

Roseau

Not to scale.

J. Raycroft

Ports of Entry

Sint Maarten/ Saint Martin:
Philipsburg, Sint Maarten
Simpson Bay, Sint Maarten
Marigot Bay, Saint Martin

St. Barts:
Gustavià

Saba:
Fort Bay
Ladder Bay

Statia:
Orenjestad

St. Kitts and Nevis:
Basseterre, St. Kitts
Charlestown, Nevis
Long Point, Nevis

Antigua and Barbuda:
English Harbour, Antigua
Falmouth Harbour, Antigua
St. John's, Antigua
Jolly Harbour, Antigua
Codrington, Barbuda

Montserrat:
Little Bay

Guadeloupe:
Deshaies, Guadeloupe
Basse Terre, Guadeloupe
Pointe à Pitre, Guadeloupe

Marie Galante:
Grande Bourg

Dominica:
Portsmouth
Roseau

J. Raycroft

Swan Base, Anse Marcel, St. Martin   J. Raycroft

(francs have been withdrawn since the instatement of the Euro) and in guilders on the Dutch side. Apparently in many places the Euro exchange is equal to the dollar (1$≈ 1 Euro). Paying with the Euro will probably be a more even exchange. Of course, as on most of the islands, credit cards are generally accepted.

Customs and Immigration

The locations of customs and immigration are as follows: Philipsburg and Simpson Bay in Dutch Sint Maarten and Marigot on French side. You must check in and out of immigration before going to each side of the island from the other.

Philipsburg:	bring your passport and ship's papers to the commercial port. You will have to pay a departure tax to leave the Dutch side. Hours for the Philipsburg port authority are as follows: Monday to Friday, 0800-1200 and 1300-1600, Sundays, 0900-1500.
Simpson Bay:	bring your passport, ship's papers and your last clearance. There will be a small departure tax to pay. Hours of operation are as follows: 0700-1800 daily.
Marigot Bay:	Hours of operation are weekdays from 0800-1200 and 1400-1800.

Airline Access

St. Martin is serviced by many different airlines, both local in the Caribbean and international.

ALM	AOM
Air France	American Airlines

KLM	Let's Travel
Liat	Maduro & Sons
Winair	Caribbean Star

Communications

Calling St. Martin from another country:
from U.S. to the French side, dial 011-590-590 + six-digit local number,
from the U.S. to the Dutch side, dial 011-599-5 + local number.
Calling out of the country:
for U.S., dial 00 + 1 + the area code and then the number.
for the U.K., dial 00 + 44 + the area code and local number.
Calling French side to Dutch side:
dial 00 then the 10-digit number.
Calling Dutch side to French side:
dial 0 then the 10-digit number.
Calling within the French side:
dial all 10 digits
Calling within the Dutch side:
dial the last 7 digits
Phone cards:
each side has public phones that take phone cards, but the cards for each side are different.
ATT direct: dial 0800-99-00-11
Internet Cafés: DC Internet Café, Sint Maarten

Medical Facilities and Emergency Numbers

Ambulance:
French side, 0590-87-74-14
Dutch side, 599-542-2111
Hospital:
French side, 0590-87-50-07
Dutch side 599-542-2300
Police:
French Marine, 0590-87-73-84
Dutch side, 599-542-2222

For more information on St. Martin, please refer to Chris Doyle's ***Cruising Guide to the Leeward Islands***. Contact Cruising Guide Publications at 800-330-9542 or www.cruisingguides.com.

St. Martin Tourism Offices:
Philipsburg:
Phone (599-554) 22 337
Fax (599-554) 22 734
Marigot:
Phone (590) 590 29 05 73
Fax (590) 590 87 56 43

Directory of Marinas & Services

French West Indies: Sint Maarten
Bobby's Marina and Boatyard, Philipsburg *(See our ad on p. 71)*   599-542-2366

Great Bay Marina, Philipsburg	599-542-5705
Island Water World,	
Cole Bay *(See our ad on the outside back cover)*	599-544-5310
Lagoon Marina, Cole Bay	599-544-5210
La Palapa Marina, Simpson Bay	
(See our ad on p. 66)	599-545-2735
Princess Yacht Club, Simpson Bay	
(See our ad on p. 67)	599-544-2953
Simpson Bay Yacht Club Marina	
(See our ad on p. 67)	599-554-2309

French West Indies: Saint Martin

Cadisco, Simpson Bay	590-66-18-98
Captain Olivers, Oyster Pond	590-87-33-47
Marina Port La Royale, Marigot Bay	590-87-20-43
Port Lonvilliers, Anse Marcel *(See our ad on p. 62)*	590-87-31-94

Directory of Boatyards & Services

Netherland Antilles: Sint Maarten
Bobby's Marina and Boatyard,
Philipsburg *(See our ad on p. 71)*   599-542-2366

French West Indies: Saint Martin

Geminga, Marigot Bay	590-29-35-52
Polypat Caraibes, Marigot Bay *(See our ad p. 69)*	590-87-12-01
Time Out Boatyard, Marigot Bay	590-52-02-88

Marigot	St. Martin	French West Indies

☑ Radio channel monitored: 16		☑ Showers: Yes
☑ Transient dockage: 50		☑ Ice: Yes
☑ Longterm dockage: 150		☑ Telephone hook-up: Yes
☐ Anchoring near marina: No		☐ TV/cable: No
☑ Dockage rate: Please call		☑ Chandlery: Yes
☑ Mooring rate: Please call		☑ Customs/Immigration: Yes
☑ Longest length: 150ft		☑ Hours: 12 hours/day
☑ Catamaran dockage: Yes		☑ Currency/Credt Cards accepted:
☑ Depth at low water: 14, 50ft		Euro and US Dollars
☑ Electricity: 220v (15 AMPS)		☑ Provisions: Yes
110v (100 AMPS)		☑ Restaurant(s): Plenty
☑ Water: Yes		☑ Bars: Plenty
☑ Fuel: Yes		☑ Computer access: Yes
☑ Pump out station: Yes		☑ Marine Services: Yes

Chris Doyle

Marigot, St. Martin

Marina Fort Louis
St. Martin, French West Indies

Phone 011-590 (0) 690-50-9257
Fax 590-590-879221
VHF Channel 16

| Anse Marcel | St. Martin | French West Indies |

☑ Radio channel monitored: 16, 11
☐ Transient dockage: n/a
☑ Longterm dockage:
☑ Anchoring near marina: Yes, in the bay Marcel Cove
☑ Dockage rate: 65¢/ft/day
☐ Mooring rate: n/a
☑ Longest length: 120ft
☑ Catamaran dockage: Yes
☑ Depth at low water: 9ft
☑ Electricity: 110v, 220v, 60 cycle
☑ Water: Yes
☑ Fuel: Yes
☐ Pump out station:
☑ Showers: Yes
☑ Ice: Yes

☐ Telephone hook-up:
☐ TV/cable:
☑ Chandlery: Yes
☐ Customs/Immigration:
☑ Hours: 8:00am - 1200am
2:00pm - 6:00pm Everyday
☑ Currency/Credt Cards accepted: Visa, MC, Euro, US Dollars
☑ Provisions: Superette
☑ Restaurant(s): Yes
☑ Bars: Yes
☑ Computer access: Yes
☑ Marine Services: Public phone, weather report, fax, copy, and washing machine

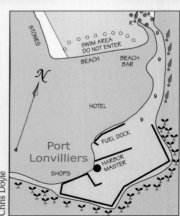

Chris Doyle

Anse Marcel

HERE! I AM
QUIET AND SECURE

Port Lonvilliers

Anse Marcel, St. Martin, French West Indies

Phone 590 87 31 94 • Fax 590 87 33 96
VHF Channel 16, 11
www.portlonvilliers.com

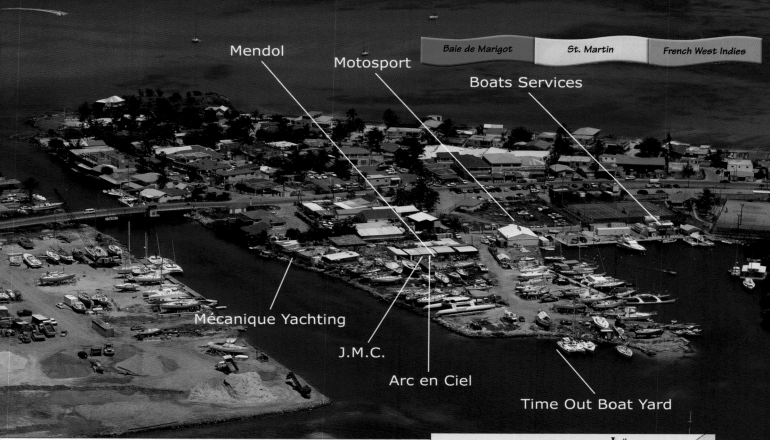

Mendol · Motosport · Boats Services

Baie de Marigot · St. Martin · French West Indies

Mécanique Yachting · J.M.C. · Arc en Ciel · Time Out Boat Yard

- ☑ Radio channel monitored: 16
- ☑ Boat accomodation: Monohull, multihull, power, over8 foot draft, 75 foot length, 13 tons
- ☑ Haul-out equipment/machinery: crane
- ☑ Haul-out fee: 35'-39' - $410 40'-45' - $580, 46'-51' - $600
- ☑ Dockage rate: $7/ft/month
- ☐ Time alotted for haul-out:
- ☑ Mechanic on premises: Yes
- ☐ Yard only work: No
- ☑ Do-it-yourself work: Yes
- ☑ Customer supplied paints/parts allowed: Yes

- ☑ Yard specialites: Haul-out, repairs, maintenance, storage
- ☐ Fuel:
- ☐ Water:
- ☐ Chandlery on premises: No, nearby
- ☐ Hours: 8:00am - 12:30pm 3:00pm - 7:30pm
- ☑ Currency/Credit Cards accepted: Euro & US dollars; no credit cards
- ☑ Associated marina: Yes
- ☑ Associated repair facilities: Yes
- ☐ Provisions:
- ☐ Other yard services:

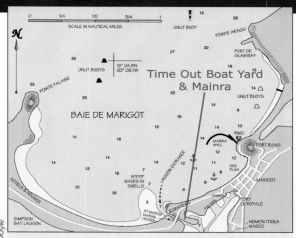

Chris Doyle

On the French side of the lagoon, located to the left side of the access canal, after the bridge.

Lagoon Entrance, Baie de Marigot

All these businesses are conveniently located around Time Out Boat Yard & Marina on the French side of St. Martin, next to the bridge of Sandy Ground at the entrance to the Lagoon.

They are dedicated to serve the cruising community, their expertise in an array of fields will cover most of your needs and for your convenience all in the same area.

These friendly professionals offer you the following services:

Time Out Boat Yard
Boat Yard & Marina
Phone 0590 52 0288
Fax 0590 52 0289
timeoutboat@hotmail.com

Arc en Ciel
Marine Upholstery
Phone 0590 29 5339
Port 0690 39 3128
alainoreille@wandoo.fr

J.M.C.
Hydraulic, Refrigeration
Dealer for:
Lecomble & Schmitt
Phone 0690 62 1521
Fax 0590 29 0979
jmcstmartin@yahoo.fr

Boats Services
Diesel & Gaz Fuel Station
Phone 0590 52 5865
Fax 0590 87 1184
boats_services@wandoo.fr

Mendol
General Engineering
Phone 0590 87 0594
Fax 0590 87 0778
mendol@wandoo.fr

Mécaniques Yachting Caraibes
Dealer for:
Man-Nanni-Iveco-Sinergie
Phone 0590 29 0655
Port 0590 27 1260
Fax 0590 51 0812

Motorsport
Mariner outboards/
Caribe inflatables Sales
& Maintenance
Phone 0590 29 0041
Fax 0590 29 0122
motsport@outremer.com

Time Out Boat Yard & Marina

Lagoon Entrance, Baie de Marigot
St. Martin, French West Indies

Phone 590-590-520288 • Fax 590-590-520289
VHF Channel 16
timeoutboat@hotmail.com

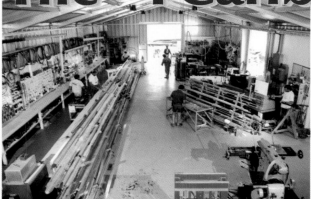

le West indies

St Martin's Shopping Mall!

CCROLAB - FOTOFORT	Photgrapher	LINEA UOMO	Men's clothing
URELIO DI ROMA	Men's clothing	LORD & HUNTER	Caribbean gifts & accessories
HARME'S	Lingerie	L'OCCITANE	Well-being products made in Provence
ONNA	Women's clothing	NEW MAN	Men's & women's clothing
OLLOW ME	Piano bar, snacks & ice cream	ORO DE SOL	Watches & jewelry
OLDFINGER	Watches & jewelry	PRIMAVERA	Limoges dishes, house linen
EOPS CAFE	Snack bar	SACHEE	Bags & luggage
ACOSTE	Men's, women's & children's clothing	SCOOP	Shoes for men & women
ANCEL	Bags & luggage	SKERZO	Women's clothing
ES DIABLOTINS	Children's clothing 0 - 14	STAR BIJOUX	Jewelry & accessories
OURMANDISES	Fine grocery	VANITY FIRST	Cosmetics
IAMOND CREATIONS	Fine jewelry, diamonds, watches & designer lines	MICHEL ROYER RESTAURANT	Exclusive gourmet cuisine

Palapa Marina
Sint Maarten

www.palapamarina.com
Phone: [599] 545-2735
Fax:[599] 545-2510
VHF#68
E-Mail: office@palapamarina.com

The Professional service provided at the Palapa Marina has created a positive yet relaxed atmosphere. Our primary function is shore side support services catering to the needs of the professional yachting community and more specifically yacht charter turn-around.

- Dockage 22 Yacht slips
- Depth - to 20ft
- Electicity - 110/220/3ph
- Fuel Bunkering
- Water
- Cable & Telephone
- Showers
- Laundry Services
- Yacht Provisioning
- Ships Agents
- Crew Placement
- Taxi, Car Limo Rental
- Scuba Shop
- Propane Refill
- Day Workers
- Courier Services

Yacht Provisioning
PALAPA MARINA

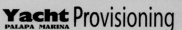

Food & Drinks Provisioning

To Order:
Phone: (599) 545-2735
Fax: (599) 545-2510
E-Mail: provisioning@palapamarina.com

Palapa Marina Service Section

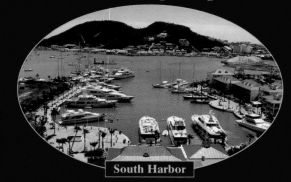

POLYPAT CARAÏBES

Situated:
On the right, just after the bridge, on the canal leading to the lagoon, on the French side of St. Martin.

The POLYPAT CARAÏBES crew will be happy to welcome you, and on site you will find everything you need for your haul-out, and other projects.

Available:
60 ton crane for haul-out and dismasting
Fiberglass repairs
Paint facilities
Osmosis treatment
Registered Gelsield agent
Dry storage and 160 feet of dockage space

Also:
Spare parts agent for major boatbuilders such as Jeanneau, Beneteau etc...
Wholesale paint dealer for INTERNATIONAL

New:
AIRLESS applicator for anti-fouling

Miscellaneous:
Electricity: 220 volts
Individual water meters
Showers and toilets

Night security guard and 24 hours on weekends

Pont de Sandy Ground BP 4012 97064 ST MARTIN
Tél: 05 90 87 12 01 - Fax: 05 90 87 22 13
e.mail: polypat.caraibes@wanadoo.fr

VINISSIMO
THE WINE & SPIRIT BOUTIQUE

Sylvain PEREIRA - Sommelier
Vinissimo, Boutique de Marigot
La Tour d'Argent (Paris) - 1991/94
Les Saveurs (London) - 1994/96

DUTY FREE - FREE DELIVERY
FREE WINE TASTING
1, Rue Low Town - Marigot
Tél/Fax : 0590 87 70 78
www.vinissimo.net

St. Barts (St. Barthelemy)

Culture

St. Barts (formally St. Barthelemy) is one of the smaller islands in the Caribbean. Just nine square miles in area, this spectacular island has achieved quite a luxurious reputation for any size. Ever wondered where the rich and famous go? The answer is St. Barts. Historically, St. Barts was discovered by Columbus and named for his brother, Bartolomeo. For many years the English, the Spanish and the French fought over this island as a firm foothold for a trading post (the island is too dry for much agriculture), and in the 1600's, pirates used the island as a base for spending and trading their spoils. In 1784, St. Barts was handed over to the Swedes in exchange for a free port in Gotenborg. Years later in 1878, King Oscar III of Sweden sold St. Barts back to the French. The island remains a free port. Just recently St. Barts has become a fabulous vacationing spot that includes a rocky backdrop for beautiful beaches and green palms.

Currency

Due to the new implementation of the Euro, St. Barts will no longer be using French francs. Prices may be quoted in either Euros or U.S. dollars, but both can generally be used. Credit cards can be used as well.

Customs and Immigration

Gustavia: you must report your arrival to the port authority as you enter via VHF 16, at which point your passports and ship's papers will be needed. Hours of the port office are as follows: 0730-1730, with a break from 1230-1430. In season the office is open Sunday mornings from 9-12. Charges will be determined (anywhere from 5-18$U.S. typically).

Airline Access

Air Caraibes	Air Guadeloupe
Air St. Barts	Air St. Thomas
Winair	

Communications

Calling St. Barts from another country:
from the U.S., dial 011-590-590 plus the six-digit number
from the U.K., dial 00 + 590 + the six-digit local number.
Calling out of St. Barts:
dial 00, the country code, then the number.
Calling within St. Barts:
dial 0590 plus the six-digit number
Phone cards: most phones take credit cards, those that don't use phone cards which can be purchased at the Post Office.
ATT direct: 0800-99-00-11
MCI: 0800-99-00-19

Medical Facilities and Emergency Numbers

Hospital de Bruyn: 0590-27-60-35
Police: 0590-27-66-66
Port Captain: 0590-27-66-97
Fire Department: 0590-27-66-13
Doctor on call: 0590-27-76-03
Pharmacie St. Barts: 0590-27-61-82

For more information on St. Barts, please refer to Chris Doyle's **Cruising Guide to the Leeward Islands**. Contact Cruising Guide Publications at 800-330-9542 or www.cruisingguides.com.

St. Barts Tourist Office:
Phone (011) 590 27 87 27
Fax (011) 590 27 74 47
B.P. 113
Gustavia, 97113
St. Barthelemy, FWI

Directory of Marinas & Services

French West Indies: Saint Barts

Port du Gustavia	590-27-66-97
St. Barth Marine, Gustavia	590-27-60-38
La Voilerie du Port Franc, St. Barts	
(See our ad on p. 75)	590-27-85-73
Le Ship du Port Franc, St. Barts	
(See our ad on p. 75)	590-27-86-29

Saba   J. Raycroft

Saba

Culture

Saba is a small enchanting island whose area is only 5 square miles, whilst, by contrast, her height reaches nearly 3,000 feet. There are only 1500 inhabitants on this little Dutch island, whose ownership changed twelve times before coming under the Kingdom of the Netherlands in 1832 for good. Often called "the unspoiled queen", Saba has an almost uninhabitable terrain. For this reason, it is one of the most pristine of all the islands in the Lesser Antilles. This island, however, is another one that has no real natural harbors and thus not many marinas or marine service facilities.

The languages spoken here include Dutch and English. Dutch is the official language, but English is spoken by nearly everyone.

Currency

The currency in Saba is the Antillian Guilder, but U.S. currency is widely accepted.

LA VOILERIE DU PORT FRANC
Tel./ Fax: (590) 27-56-58
Email: alexaber@wanadoo.fr

LE BRIGANTIN
Tel.: (590) 27-99-95 / Fax: (590) 27-85-73
Email: leship@wanadoo.fr

La Compagnie Commerciale du Port Franc

ST BARTH MARINE
(Gas Station)
Tel:(590) 27-85-73

LA CAVE DU PORT FRANC
Tel./Fax : (590) 27-65-27
Email: lacaveduportfranc@hotmail.com

LE SHIP DU PORT FRANC
Tel: (590) 27-86-29/Fax: (590) 27-85-73
Email: leship@wanadoo.fr

Customs and Immigration

There is no customs because Saba is a free port, but one must clear in at the harbor office in Fort Baai as well as the Saba Marine Park in Ladder Baai.

Airline Access

Winair   Windward Express Airways

Only these two airlines will fly to the little airstrip on Saba, but you can catch one of many major airlines to St. Martin and then take one of the above to Saba.

Communications

Calling Saba from another country:
from the U.S., dial 011 + 599 + 4 for Saba, + 5-digit local number
from the U.K., dial 00 + 599 + 4 + 5-digit local number.
Calling another country from Saba:
to the U.S., dial 00 + 1 + area code and 7-digit local number
to the U.K., dial 00 + 44 + city code and local number
Calling Saba from another island in the Netherland Antillies:
dial 04 + 5-digit local number
Calling within Saba:
dial only 5-digit number

Medical Facilities and Emergency Numbers

Saba radio has been replaced by Curacao radio via channel 16. However, Curacao radio has means to connections for any kind of emergency in Saba.

Edwards Medical Center: 599-416-3288/9

For more information on Saba, please refer to Chris Doyle's **Cruising Guide to the Leeward Islands**. Contact Cruising Guide Publications at 800-330-9542 or www.cruisingguides.com.

Saba Tourist Office:
Saba Tourist Bureau:
Phone (599) 4-62231, Fax (599) 4-62350

Statia (St. Eustatius)

Culture

In the 18th century, Statia (full name St. Eustatius) was the trade capital for the Caribbean. The island provided an official means by which one might buy and sell goods to countries otherwise illegal to trade with. The isle itself changed ownership some 20 times. However, for several centuries Statia has remained Dutch. Presently, Statia's reputation for being the trade capital of the Indies has weakened to a mere 2,100 inhabitants (the island is only 12 square miles), and a very, very small tourist trade. If you want peace and quiet, Statia is the place to go. Though she is a Dutch island, most speak English as well.

Currency

The Netherlands Antilles guilder or florin is the main form of currency, but U.S. dollars are accepted everywhere.

Customs and Immigration

Customs and immigration is at the end of the main town dock. Office hours are 8am-5pm. There is up to a 15$ entry fee, and an additional 10$ per night park fee as well.

Airline Access

The following airlines offer access from either St. Martin or Saba to Statia. Many major airlines serve St. Martin, where you can make the connection.

Winair   Golden Rock Airways

Communications

Calling Statia from another country:
from the U.S., dial 011 + 599 + 3 + the 6-digit local number
from the U.K., dial 00 + 599 + 3 + the 6-digit local number
Calling another country from Statia:
to the U.S., dial 00 + 1 + area code and 7-digit local number
to the U.K., dial 00 + 44 + city code and local number.
Calling Statia from another Dutch island:
dial 03 + the 6-digit number.
Calling within Statia:
leave off 5993, and just dial the 6-digit number.

Medical Facilities and Emergency Numbers

Marine Park: 599-318-2884
Princess Beatrix Hospital: 599-318-2211
Port Authority: 599-318-2888

J. Raycroft

For more information on Statia, please refer to Chris Doyle's **Crusing Guide to the Leeward Islands**.Contact Cruising Guide Publications at 800-330-9542 or www.cruisingguides.com.

Statia Tourism Office: 599-318-2433
Fax: 599-318-2324

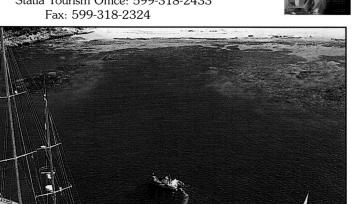

J. Raycroft

St. Kitts and Nevis

Culture

Officially *the Federation of St. Christopher and Nevis*, this two-island nation is a great haven for vacationers. Geographically, both islands have much to offer including steep mountain ranges, dense tropical rain forests, fertile valleys, beaches, and clear water. Traditionally British since the 18th century, St. Kitts, named for Christopher Columbus' patron saint, and Nevis are rich with old plantation houses and remnants of colonialism from earlier centuries, many of which have been converted to resorts and museums in more recent years. Whilst St. Kitts is larger and more populated (35,000 inhabitants for 68 square miles), Nevis is more remote and exotic. Nevis, an island nearly circular in shape, is home to wild monkeys, birds, a beautiful array of island wildlife and only 9,000 humans. Both islands offer exquisite snorkeling and diving and miles of beaches, perfect for vacationing.

Currency

The currency in Nevis and St. Kitts is the EC (Eastern Caribbean) dollar.

Customs and Immigration

The nation of Nevis and St. Kitts has two ports of entry, one on each island.

St. Kitts: the port of entry is located in Basseterre, the capital. Hours are Monday through Friday 6am-5pm, 6am-9am on Saturday, and 3pm-5pm on Sundays. There is a 10$ EC entry charge and an additional $20 EC yacht charge. Additional dues are collected for yachts over 20 tons.

Nevis: the main port of entry in Nevis is at Charlestown. Hours are weekdays from 8am-12pm. There is also a port at Long Point which is open weekdays from 8am-4pm and Saturdays from 8am-10am.

Airline Access

St. Kitts:

American Airlines	BWIA
Kantours	LIAT
Nevis Express	TDC Airline Service
Tropical Tours	Winair

Nevis:

Evelyn's Travel	Nevis Express

Communications

Calling Nevis and St. Kitts from another country:
from the U.S., dial 1 + 869 + the 7-digit local number
from the U.K., dial 00 + 1 + 869 + the 7-digit local number
Calling another country from Nevis and St. Kitts:
to the U.S., dial 1 + area code and 7-digit local number
to the U.K., dial 011 + 44 + city code and local number
Calling St. Kitts/Nevis from within the islands:
dial last 7 digits
Phone cards can be bought at local Cable & Wireless stores open on weekdays.

Medical Facilities and Emergency Numbers

Nevis:
Nevis Port Authority: 869-469-5521/5419
Dr. Dias: 869-469-5455
Evelyn's Drug Store: 869-469-5278

St. Kitts:
Customs: 869-465-2521
City Drug: 869-465-2156
Dr. Kathleen Allen: 869-465-5348

For more information on Nevis and St. Kitts, please refer to Chris Doyle's **Cruising Guide to the Leeward Islands**. Contact Cruising Guide Publications at 800-330-9542 or www.cruisingguides.com.

Nevis and St. Kitts:Tourism Offices
Department of Tourism (St. Kitts):
869-465-2620/4040
Nevis Tourism Bureau: 869-469-1042
St. Kitts and Nevis Hotel and Tourism Association:
869-465-5304

Directory of Marinas & Services

West Indies: St. Kitts
Port Zante, Basseterre   869-466-5021

West Indies: Nevis
New Castle Bay Marina   869-465-9373

Montserrat

Culture

Montserrat is an English territory located almost in the center of the Leeward Island chain. It has been dubbed the 'Emerald Isle' for both its Irish history and its verdant terrain. In 1995, however, a volcano located on the South end of the island erupted laying the town of Plymouth to waste. Thus, there is a sharp contrast between the rugged newness of volcanic terrain on the South end, and the green lushness and beauty of the North end. Nevertheless, the volcanic activity has far from frightened off Montserrat's habitants. 5,000 still live on the island, mostly on the North end since the South has been somewhat unpredictable due to the Soufriere Hills volcano's activity. The island is, however, one of the most beautiful in all of the Caribbean, and tourism is quickly returning. There aren't that many natural harbors in Montserrat and thus there is a lack of sufficient marinas and boatyards. This should not keep one from sailing her beautiful waters, though. There is a restriction around the bottom half of the island that should be carefully adhered to. An exclusion zone exists from the shore to two miles out to sea surrounding the southern half of Montserrat. Volcanic activity can be monitored weekly on Radio Montserrat (91.1) on Fridays at 7:30 pm.

Currency

Currency on this English-speaking island is the EC (Eastern Caribbean) dollar. Credit cards can be used at most major establishments.

Customs and Immigration

The port of entry is in Little Bay. Customs, the Port Authority, and Immigration are all by the port entrance. There is a $35 EC port authority fee. Hours are Monday through Friday, 8am-4pm. Officers can be found after hours and on weekends.

Airline Access

There is only access to Montserrat via helicopter and ferry from Antigua. However, many international airlines fly in to Antigua.

Helicopters:
Carib Aviation   Montserrat Aviation Services
Caribbean Helicopters
Ferries:
Opale Express

Communications

Montserrat has an area code of 664
Calling Montserrat from other countries:
    from the U.S., dial 1 + 664 + local 7-digit number
    from the U.K., dial 00 + 1 + 664 + local 7-digit number.
Calling other countries from Montserrat:
    to the U.S., dial 1 + area code and 7-digit local number
    to the U.K., dial 011 + 44 + city code and local number
Calling within Montserrat: dial 7-digit number
Phone cards can be attained at Cable and Wireless.

Medical Facilities and Emergency Numbers

Main hospital: 664-491-2836
Emergency and Accident: 664-491-2802
Police: 664-491-2555
Port Authority: 664-491-2791

Montserrat Volcano Observatory: 664-491-5647
For more information on Montserrat, please refer to Chris Doyle's **Cruising Guide to the Leeward Islands**. Contact Cruising Guide Publications at 800-330-9542 or www.cruising-guides.com.
Montserrat Tourist Office: 664-491-2230

English Harbour, Antigua   J. Raycroft

Antigua and Barbuda

Culture

Antigua and Barbuda have been considered one country, independent since 1981 when England let her change from associated commonwealth to independent nation. The islands are still both predominantly English-speaking. Though Antigua has been booming in tourism (the largest source for income) for quite some time, Barbuda, only a little over half Antigua's size, has a mere 1600 inhabitants and is terribly opposed to tourism. Barbuda is completely lined with beach, and has a highest point of only 125 feet above sea level. The inhabitants of Barbuda live in the only village, Codrington.

Antigua, however, is much larger and much more bustling. There are over 67,000 residents on this 108 square mile island, and many resorts and hotels. It is no small wonder that this island is so popular, though. This island is fringed with palms and beaches, visited by warm winds, lapped by azure waves.

Currency

Antigua and Barbuda use the EC (Eastern Caribbean) dollar. You can also usually pay in US dollars, and credit cards are accepted.

Customs and Immigration

You may enter the island nation of Antigua and Barbuda in several places and once in will receive a cruising permit for both Antiguan and Barbudan waters.

Antigua

English Harbour and Falmouth Harbour: Bring the ship's papers to the custom's office. The offices are at Nelson's Dockyard open from 8am to 4pm every day. Entry charges range from 10-20 EC dollars depending on the length of your boat.
Cruising permits are automatic but will cost 20-30 EC dollars also depending on boat length.

St. Johns: Port Authority is at the deep water dock where customs is, open from 6am to 7pm daily.

Barbuda

Codrington: You can anchor in any harbor, but the port authority is in Codrington. You can clear here for Barbudan and Antiguan waters.

Airline Access

Air Canada	Air France
Air Jamaica	American Airlines
American Eagle	BWIA
British Airways	Continental
LIAT	Lufthansa
Caribbean Star	

Communications

Antigua and Barbuda work on a similar phone system as the U.S. with an area code of 268.

Calling Antigua and Barbuda from another country:
from the U.S., dial 1 + 268 + local 7-digit number
from the U.K., dial 00 + 1 + 268 + 7-digit local number

Calling out of country:
to the U.S., dial 1 + area code + 7-digit local number
to the U.K., dial 011 + 44 + city code and local number

Calling within the country of Antigua and Barbuda:
dial last 7 digits of number.

Internet Cafés:
Mad Max, Antigua, 268-562-4653
Antigua Cyberstop, Falmouth Harbour, 268-463-2662

Emergency Numbers and Medical Facilities

General Emergency: 999 or 911
Medical Emergency: 268-462-1975/409-5778/460-8786
Antigua and Barbuda Search and Rescue (ABSAR):
268-562-1234

For more information on Antigua and Barbuda, please refer to Chris Doyle's *Cruising Guide to the Leeward Islands*. Contact Cruising Guide Publications at 800-330-9542 or www.cruisingguides.com.

Department of Tourism
P.O. Box 363
Thames Street
St. Johns, Antigua, W.I.
(268) 462-0480, F: (268) 462-2483,
1-888-268-4227

Directory of Marinas & Services

West Indies: Antigua & Barbuda

Antigua Slipway, Ltd., English Harbour
(See our ad on p. 79)   268-460-1056

Antigua Yacht Club Marina,
Falmouth Harbour *(See our ad on p. 84)*   268-460-1543

Catamaran Marina, Falmouth Harbour   268-460-1503

Crabb's Slipway and Marina, St. John's   268-463-2113

Falmouth Harbour Marina   268-460-6054

HBP Limited Slipway and Marina,
Crabbs Peninsula   268-463-2113

English Harbour	Antigua	West Indies

- ☑ Radio channel monitored: 68,12
- ☐ Transient dockage:
- ☐ Longterm dockage:
- ☑ Anchoring near marina: Yes English Harbour
- ☐ Dockage rate:
- ☐ Mooring rate:
- ☐ Longest length: 15-25ft
- ☐ Catamaran dockage:
- ☐ Depth at low water:
- ☑ Electricity: 110v, 208v
- ☑ Water: Yes
- ☑ Fuel: Yes
- ☐ Pump out station:
- ☑ Showers: Yes
- ☑ Ice: Yes
- ☐ Telephone hook-up: No
- ☐ TV/cable: No
- ☑ Chandlery: Yes
- ☑ Customs/Immigration: Yes
- ☑ Hours: Fuel Dock Schandlery: 7:00am - 4:00pm Office Hours: 8:00am - 5:00pm
- ☑ Currency/Credit Cards accepted: Visa, MC, AmX
- ☐ Provisions:
- ☑ Restaurant(s): Catherine's Café
- ☐ Bars:
- ☐ Computer access: No
- ☑ Marine Services: Yes

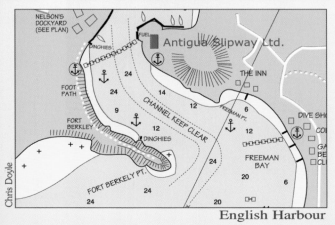

English Harbour

Chris Doyle

Directory of Marinas & Services (Continued...)

Jolly Harbour *(See our ad on p. 81)*	268-462-6042
Nelson's Dockyard Quay, English Harbour	268-460-1053
Redcliffe Quay Marina, St. John's	268-462-1847
St. James Club Marina, Mamora Bay	268-460-5000

Directory of Boatyards & Services

West Indies: Antigua & Barbuda

Crabb's Slipway and Marina, St. John's	268-463-2113
Jolly Harbour *(See our ad on p. 81)*	268-462-6042

J. Raycroft

Jolly Harbour Resort, Marina, Boatyard and Golf Club

waterfront living at its best

Located in Antigua, "The Heart of the Caribbean," Jolly Harbour Marina boasts as
"THE MOST COMPLETE MARINE FACILITY IN THE CARIBBEAN"
Nested in a quiet cove on the southwestern side of Antigua, the Jolly Harbour Marina offers the yachting community a wide range of services in walking distance from the moment you arrive. Shops, restaurants, bars, golf course, tennis courts, villas and the beach will all prepare you for a memorable and enjoyable stay.

Marina & Boatyard
Customs & Immigration clearance, Hurricane safe location. 158 slips-102 fully serviced, including super yacht dock handling vessels up to 260'. Fuel dock (duty free fuel available with 48hrs. notice), electric, water, ice, and dockside services.
Full service boatyard — 70 ton Travelift, 20 ton Knjipsta boat mover, Mobile crane, forklift.
Hard stands and keel hole berths offer the safest storage.
Contractors on-site to assist, if needed, with your yacht improvements needs
— Antifoul, Boat management, Carpentry,
Chandlery, Electrical/Refrigeration, Fabrication, Fiberglass, Osmosis treatment,
Painting/awlgrip and Rigging.

Modern Shopping Centre
Boutiques, supermarket, waterfront restaurants & bars, hairdresser, household and hardware, travel agency, dive shop, boat, bike, golf cart & car rentals, bank, art galleries, electronics, casino.

First Class Sports & Recreation Centre
Squash, tennis, 30 metre swimming pool, basketball, beachfront recreation, restaurant and bar.
Golf Course...71 par - 18 hole challenging course, pro-golf shop, bar & restaurant.
Helipad...Daily island tours or special trips can be booked on helicopters.
Villa Sales...2 bedroom waterfront and golf view villas starting at US$ 149,000.
Villa Rentals...Fully furnished, self contained privately owned beachfront villas
starting at US$125+ 18.5% nightly (high season).
Boat Sales...Sales agent on site for Searay, Boston Whaler, cruising yachts
Boat Rentals...Daily power boat rentals can be booked on site

For more information contact: Jolly Harbour, P.O. Box 1793, Antigua
MARINA Direct: (268) 462-6042 • Fax: (268) 462-7703
email: jollymarina@candw.ag • website: jollyharbour-marina.com
VHF 68 "Jolly Harbour Marina"
Refer to Cruising Guide Publications Advert when contacting Jolly Harbour.

| Falmouth Harbour | Antigua | West Indies |

☑ Radio channel monitored: 68
☑ Transient dockage: 40 slips
☑ Longterm dockage: 40 slips
☑ Anchoring near marina: Yes
  Mooring balls available
☐ Dockage rate:
☐ Mooring rate:
☑ Longest length: 320ft
☑ Catamaran dockage: Yes
☑ Depth at low water: 23ft
☑ Electricity: 110/220/380/3 phase
☑ Water: Yes
☑ Fuel: Yes (Duty free)
☐ Pump out station: No
☐ Showers: No
☑ Ice: Yes
☑ Telephone hook-up: Yes
☑ TV/cable: Yes

☑ Chandlery: Yes
☐ Customs/Immigration: No
☐ Hours: 8:00am - 5:00pm
  M - Sun. (June - Nov.)
  9:00am - 3:00pm M - F
☑ Currency/Credt Cards accepted:
  Visa, MC, AmX
☑ Provisions: Yes
☑ Restaurant(s): Southern Cross,
  Seabreeze Café, Skullduggery, La
  Lemming
☑ Bars: Seabreeze Café, Skullduggery
  Southern Cross, Last Lemming
☑ Computer access: Yes
☑ Marine Services: marine insuranc
  boutique, travel agency, liquor/su
  market, Internet café, chandlery,
  bookstore, cable & wireless

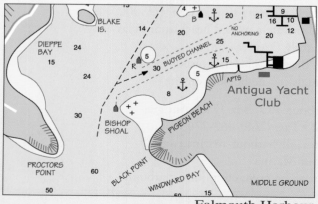

Falmouth Harbour

Chris Doyle

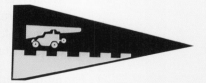

Guadeloupe

Guadeloupe is a very beautiful lush island. It has many features including a lowlands (confusingly named "Grande Terre" (highlands") and, you guessed it, a fairly mountainous region called "Basse Terre" or yep, lowlands. Separating these two regions is a river, the Rivière Salée. In the mountainous region there are waterfalls and rainforest in which one can swim and hike. The island is shaped like a butterfly and in close proximity are the islands Marie Galante and the Isles des Saintes, all of which are French. Historically, Guadeloupe was at one time (several millenia ago) inhabited by the Caribs. It wasn't until the 17th century when the French showed up that battles ensued for the right to ownership of the island. Though there were many battles with both the Caribs and the Spanish, and for a brief while the British, eventually the French pulled through leaving it, as of 1974, a department of France. Guadeloupe is a beautiful island, still very much a part of France culturally. The languages spoken are primarily French and Creole with a smattering of English in the necessary places.

Currency

Guadeloupe did pretty much only use the French Franc, but now uses the Euro almost exclusively, also accepting credit cards.

Customs and Immigration

Guadeloupe has customs offices in the following ports: Dashaies, Basse Terre, and Pointe à Pitre. Marie Galante also has a customs office, though it often is not open. The Iles des Saintes have no customs offices, but so far it has not been a problem to stay there before clearing in at Guadeloupe. There is no charge for entering the country.

Deshaies:	the customs office here does not take usual hours so it might be necessary to clear in or out at some other port. Make sure to bring your ship's papers and crew's passports, etc. with you.
Basse Terre:	hours for the customs near Marina Rivière Sens are usually 6am- 8pm, Monday through Saturday.
Pointe à Pitre:	Customs is open on weekdays only from 8am-4pm. Customs is closed Tuesday afternoon and immigration is closed Wednesday afternoon.

Airline Access

Air Liberte	Air Tropical
Air Canada	Air Caraibes
Air France	Air Guadeloupe
Air Martinique	Air St. Martin
Alpha Aviation	American Airlines
AOM Guadeloupe	Caribbean Helicopters
Corsair	Heli Inter Caraibes
LIAT	Marie Galante Aviation
Oceair	

Communications

Guadeloupe's area code is 590.
Calling Guadeloupe from another country:
from the U.S., dial 011 + 590 + 590 and then the 6-digit number
from the U.K., dial 00 + 590 + local 6-digit number

Calling out of Guadeloupe:
to the U.S., dial 00 + 1 + the area code & number
to the U.K., dial 00 + 44 + the city code & local number
Calling locally, new policy:
you must dial 0590 plus the six-digit number.
Phone cards are available at post offices.

Medical Facilities and Emergency Numbers

Medical Clinic: 0590-90-88-92
Medical Emergency Service: 0590-91-39-39
Hospital: 0590-81-71-87
COSMA: (lifeguard) 0590-71-92-92

For more information on Guadeloupe, Marie Galantes and Iles Des Saintes, please refer to Chris Doyle's **Cruising Guide to the Leeward Islands**.Contact Cruising Guide Publications at 800-330-9542 or www.cruisingguides.com.
Guadeloupe Tourist Offices:
Point à Pitre: Phone, 0590 82-09-30
Fax, 0590 83-89-22
Basseterre: Phone, 0590 81-24-83
St. Francois: Phone, 0590 88-48-74

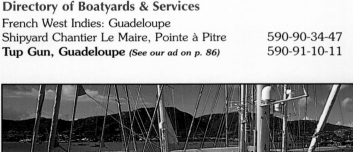

Directory of Marinas & Services

French West Indies: Guadeloupe

Cape Sud Chantier (Guadeloupe Boatyard), Pointe à Pitre	590-90-77-36
Chantier Naval Patrick Fourbin, Pointe à Pitre	590-83-21-34
Marina de Riviere Sens, Basse Terre	590-81-77-61
Marina Grand Saline, Pointe à Pitre	590-88-47-28
Port de Plaisance Marina Bas du Fort, Pointe à Pitre (See our ad on p. 85)	590-90-84-85
Shipyard Chantier Le Maire, Pointe à Pitre	590-90-34-47

Directory of Boatyards & Services

French West Indies: Guadeloupe

Shipyard Chantier Le Maire, Pointe à Pitre	590-90-34-47
Tup Gun, Guadeloupe (See our ad on p. 86)	590-91-10-11

J. Raycroft

- ☑ Radio channel monitored: 9
- ☑ Transient dockage: 200 slips
- ☑ Longterm dockage: 350 slips
- ☑ Anchoring near marina: Yes, contact the harbour's office
- ☑ Dockage rate: 25Euro/day, 336Euro/month (40ft long)
- ☐ Mooring rate:
- ☐ Longest length: 160ft
- ☑ Catamaran dockage: Yes
- ☑ Depth at low water: 14-80ft
- ☑ Electricity: 110v, 220v, 380v
- ☑ Water: Yes
- ☑ Fuel: Yes
- ☑ Pump out station: Yes
- ☑ Showers: Yes
- ☑ Ice: Yes
- ☐ Telephone hook-up: No
- ☐ TV/cable: No
- ☑ Chandlery: Yes
- ☑ Customs/Immigration: Yes
- ☑ Hours: 8:00am - 6:00pm Monday - Sunday
- ☑ Currency/Credit Cards accepted: Visa, Euro
- ☑ Provisions: Full service
- ☑ Restaurant(s): Large choice
- ☑ Bars: Large choice
- ☑ Computer access: Yes
- ☑ Marine Services: Boatyard with lift, all kinds of offered services, work shops and engineering.

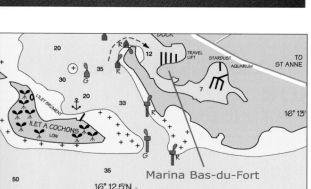

Chris Doyle

Pointe à Pitre

88

J. Raycroft

| Folie-Anse Beach | Marie-Galante | Guadeloupe |

☑ Radio channel monitored: 69
☐ Transient dockage:
☐ Longterm dockage:
☑ Anchoring near marina: Yes, 10 bouys available at Folle-Anse's beach
☐ Dockage rate:
☑ Mooring rate: 15 Euro/day
☐ Longest length:
☐ Catamaran dockage:
☑ Depth at low water: 14-80ft
☐ Electricity: No
☑ Water: Yes
☑ Fuel: Yes
☐ Pump out station: No
☐ Showers: No
☑ Ice: Yes
☐ Telephone hook-up: No

☐ TV/cable: No
☐ Chandlery: No, Bosco
☐ Customs/Immigration: No
☐ Hours:
☑ Currency/Credt Cards accepted: Visa, MC, AmX,
☑ Provisions: Morning delivery of fresh fruits, vegetables, bread and croissants
☑ Restaurant(s): Yes
☑ Bars: Yes
☑ Computer access: Yes
☑ Marine Services: Taxi Boat to St. Louis or other places on Marie-Galante, snorkeling, windsurfing, Hobie-Cat, and e-mail box

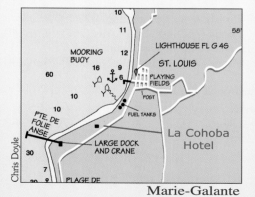

Chris Doyle

Marie-Galante

La Cohoba Hotel

Folle-Anse Beach, Marie-Galante, Guadeloupe, FWI

Phone (590) 590 97 5050 • Fax (590) 590 97 9796
VHF Channel 69
cohoba@leaderhotels.gp • www.leader-hotels.gp

Dominica

Culture

Dominica is a beautiful and incredibly verdant island. Roughly 290 square miles in area, Dominica carries a population of about 86,000 people. Due to the shape of the island, there aren't actually that many natural harbors, though certainly still there are many worthwhile anchorages. Perhaps this is justified by the fact that Dominica's interior is filled with insurmountable beauty including waterfalls, rainforests, green peaks shrouded in clouds, and frequent rainbows, not to mention a coastline with beaches, palms and plenty of sunshine. However, if you're looking for a hot tourist spot, Dominica is not the place. The island is a natural paradise with very few resorts, though it is a cruise ship port. Her wonders lie in the rainforests, Trafalgar Falls, the boiling lake, the mountains, the valleys, and 365 rivers.

Dominica gained independence from Great Britain in 1978 and is now a part of The Commonwealth of Nations and is predominantly English speaking.

Dominica   J. Raycroft

Currency

The currency in Dominica is the EC or the Eastern Caribbean dollar, but US dollars are also widely accepted. Credit cards and Traveler's Checks are also widely used and accepted.

Customs and Immigration

Customs and Immigration are located in the capital of Roseau and also Portsmouth in Prince Rupert Bay. Both offices are open Mondays 8am-1pm, 2pm-5pm, and Tuesday-Friday 8am-1pm, 2pm-4pm. Immigration may not be necessary. Make sure to have copies of the crew list and the passenger list. Departure tax is 12$EC.

Airline Access

Air Guadeloupe	American Eagle
LIAT	Air Caraibe
Caribbean Star	Cardinal Air

Communications

Dominica's area code is 767.
Calling Dominica from another country:
    from the U.S., dial 1 + 767 + the 7-digit local number
    from the U.K., dial 00 + 1 + 767 + the 7-digit local number
Calling another country from Dominica:
    to the U.S., dial 1 + area code and 7-digit local number
    to the U.K., dial 011 + 44 + city code and local number
Calling within Dominica:
    dial 7-digit number
Calling cards available or dial 1-800-872-2881 for USA direct.
Internet Cafés:
    Surf Café Domnik, Roseau, 767-235-6987
    Cornerhouse Café, Roseau, 767-449-9000

Medical Facilities and Emergency Numbers

Police, Fire and Ambulance 999
Grand Bay Hospital 446-3706
Marigot Hospital 445-7091
Portsmouth Hospital 445-5237
Roseau (Princess Margaret Hospital) 448-2231

For more information on Dominica, please refer to Chris Doyle's *Cruising Guide to the Leeward Islands*. Contact Cruising Guide Publications at 800-330-9542 or www.cruisingguides.com.

Dominica Tourist Offices:
    National Development Corporation:
        Phone (767) 448-2045, Fax (767) 448-5840
    Dominica Hotel and Tourism Association:
        Phone (767) 448-6565, Fax (767) 448-0299

Directory of Marinas & Services

West Indies: Dominica
Castaways Marina, Mero   767-449-6244

Isles des Saintes

J. Raycroft

WINDWARD ISLANDS

St. Georges Harbour, Grenada

Ravcroft

These Verdant, Tropical Islands with Lofty Mountains are at the Southern End of the Eastern Caribbean Island Arch

The Windward Islands are a fascinating destination for cruisers. They consist of four major islands, Martinique, St. Lucia, St. Vincent and Grenada, and quite a few small ones as well. All the islands provide safe anchorages and harbors, thereby allowing for day-sails and pleasure cruising. Each island, however, has its own distinct charm and flavor, owing to different historical backgrounds. Whilst St. Lucia, St. Vincent and the Grenadines, and Grenada and Carriacou are all independent nations, Martinique is a French department, who's capital is the largest city in the French West Indies.

Geographically, the four main islands of the Windwards are relatively large. Each island is richly tropical with a rain forest interior surrounded by mountains often shrouded in clouds. Toward the shores of these islands are beaches and palms truly characteristic of the Caribbean. There is a quite a distance between the larger islands, and thus sailing from one to another can be more challenging, as the wind is brisker and therefore the wave action is more apparent.

Martinique

Culture

Martinique is a beautiful blend of French and Creole culture. Due to its status as a department of France, Martinique is in many ways an extension of France in language and lifestyle. However, outside of the towns, Martinique is as much an island as any other in the Caribbean, with a heavy cultural influence of West Indian Creole. Though this island is home to the largest city in the French West Indies, Fort-de-France, a considerable portion of Martinique is devoted to growing pineapples, bananas and sugar cane, and much like the other Windward Islands, is mountainous and forested.

Much of Martinique's history was spent under the French flag. When the island was first discovered by Europeans in the late 15th century, it was inhabited by Carib Indians. Soon, however, French settlers colonized much of the island and would do so for the remainder of her history with exception of maybe twenty years when the British seized control. Intermittent British control was nevertheless advantageous for the island because it allowed Martinique to avoid the French Revolution. When the French regained control, the war was over, and in 1946, the island would officially become a department of France. Languages spoken on the island include French, French Creole patois, and some English.

Currency

The major currency used in Martinique at this time is the Euro, however U.S. dollars, traveler's checks and major credit cards are also widely accepted.

St. Pierre

MARTINIQUE

Fort de France

Marin

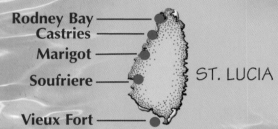

Rodney Bay
Castries
Marigot
Soufriere

ST. LUCIA

Vieux Fort

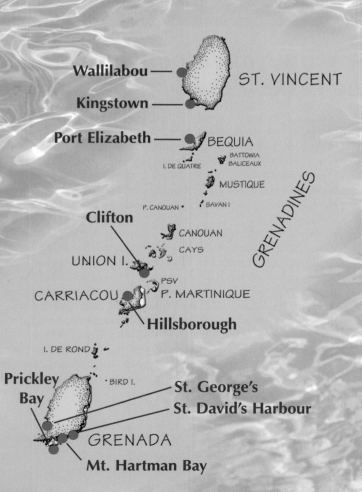

Wallilabou

ST. VINCENT

Kingstown

Port Elizabeth
BEQUIA
BATTOWIA
BALICEAUX
I. DE QUATRE
MUSTIQUE
P. CANOUAN
SAVAN I

GRENADINES

Clifton
CANOUAN
CAYS

UNION I.
PSV
CARRIACOU
P. MARTINIQUE

Hillsborough

I. DE ROND

BIRD I.

Prickley Bay

St. George's
St. David's Harbour

GRENADA

Mt. Hartman Bay

Not to scale.

94

Ports of Entry

Martinique:
Fort de France, Martinique
Marin, Martinique
St. Pierre, Martinique

St. Lucia:
Rodney Bay, St. Lucia
Castries, St. Lucia
Marigot Bay, St. Lucia
Vieux Fort, St. Lucia
Soufriere, St. Lucia

St. Vincent:
Wallilabou
Kingstown

The Grenadines:
Port Elizabeth, Bequia
Clifton, Union Island

Grenada:
St. George's
Prickley Bay
Mt. Hartman Bay
St. David's Harbour

Carriacou:
Hillsborough

Grenada

J. Raycroft

Customs and Immigration

The main customs office is located in Fort de France, however clearance is also available in Marin and St. Pierre. Customs is open 7:30am-11am, and 2:30pm-5pm daily.

Airline Access

Air Calypso	Air France
Air Guadeloupe	Air Martinique
American Airlines	BWIA
LIAT	

Communications

All Martinique numbers are 10-digits beginning with either 0596 or 0696 (mobile phones) with a 6-digit local number. When calling from another country, the first (0) should be left off.

Calling Martinique from another country:
from the U.S., dial 011 + 596 + 596 (or 696) + 6-digit local number
from the U.K., dial 00 + 596 (or 696) + 6-digit local number

Calling another country from Martinique:
to the U.S., dial 00 + 1 + area code and local number
to the U.K., dial 00 + 44 + city code and local number

Calling within Martinique:
dial 0596 + 6-digit local number

International operator: 3650

Card phones are available all over the island. Cards can be bought in post offices, change houses, and most newspaper stands.

Internet Cafés:
Tursiops Caraibes, Anses D'Arlet, (0596) 68 74 22
Definitel Micro, Blvd Allegre
The Web Café, Fort de France
Balade de Mer, Marin
Sud Bureautique, Marin

Medical Facilities and Emergency Numbers

Ambulance: (0596) 75 15 75
Fire: 18
Police: 17, headquarters: (0596) 63 00 00
Clinic: (0596) 71 82 85
COSMA (lifeboat): (0596) 71 92 92
Customs:
Fort de France, (0596) 71 83 06
Marin (0596) 74 91 64
Hospital: (0596) 50 15 15
Medical Emergency: (0596) 63 33 33/ 60 60 44

For more information on Martinique, please refer to Chris Doyle's **Sailor's Guide to the Windward Islands**. Contact Cruising Guide Publications at 800-330-9542 or www.cruisingguides.com.

Tourist Office: Fort de France, (0596) 63 79 60

Directory of Marinas & Services

Windward Islands: Martinique

Marin Yacht Harbor	596-748383
Le Ponton, Anse Mitan	596-661730
Port de Plaisance, du Marin (See our ad on p. 99)	596-748383
Somatras Marina, Anse Mitan	596-660774

Directory of Boatyards & Services

Windward Islands: Martinique

CarenAntilles, Fort de France (See our ad on p. 98)	596-63-76-74
Martinique Dry Dock, Fort de France, Quai Ouest	596-72-69-40
Multicap Caraibes, Fort de France, Quai Ouest	596-71-41-81

Bequia

J. Raycroft

St. Lucia

Culture

Although St. Lucia has been under British ownership for several centuries, culturally in many ways the island is French. St. Lucia was first settled almost 2,000 years ago by Arawak Indians. Around 800A.D., the Carib Indians took their place. When the Europeans discovered the island circa 1500, the Caribs were still there. Settlements on St. Lucia weren't really successful until the mid 17th century. After several attempts by the British to colonize, the French finally stepped in and purchased St. Lucia for the French West India Company. However, battles between the French and English for St. Lucia would continue until 1814 when the British finally won the island. In 1979, St. Lucia finally became independent within the British Commonwealth.

St. Lucia is a 239 square mile island known worldwide for its beauty. The Pitons, twin peaks that reach a height of 2000 feet, jut steeply and dramatically from the sea near Soufriere. There is rain forest, an incredible variety of wildlife, boiling lakes and sulfur vents, waterfalls and much more to be discovered. St. Lucia offers all the typical Caribbean amenities: beach, forest, plantations, mountains, beautiful reefs and diving, not to mention the incredible French-Creole culture and people. Languages spoken are English and French Patois.

Currency

St. Lucia uses EC (Eastern Caribbean) dollars. Major credit cards and traveler's checks are widely accepted. ATM's are also available.

Customs and Immigration

Customs is in the following locations:

Rodney Bay	Castries
Marigot Bay	Vieux Fort
Soufriere	

Hours are weekdays 8am-12:15pm, 1:30-3:45. A fee is charged for off-hours.

Entry charges:$15EC navigational aids, $10EC and clearance fees of $5-$15EC depending on the size of the vessel. Yachts on charter pay between $20EC and $40EC.

Airline Access

Air Canada	Air Martinique
American Airlines	American Eagle
British Airways	BWIA
Caribbean Star	Eagle Air Services
LIAT	US Air
Virgin Atlantic	

Communications

St. Lucian numbers are like those in the U.S. with an area code of 758 and a 7-digit local number.

Calling St. Lucia from another country:
from the U.S., dial 1 + 758 + 7-digit local number
from the U.K., dial 00 + 1 + 758 + 7-digit local number
Calling another country from St. Lucia:
to the U.S., dial 1 + area code + 7-digit local number
to the U.K., dial 011 + 44 + city code and local number
Calling within St. Lucia: dial 7-digit local number

Grenada, Windward Islands   J. Raycroft

Operator: 0
Payphones use cards that are available to purchase in selected shops.

Internet Cafés:
C.T.L. Rent-a-Car, 452-0732
Jambe de Bois, 452-0321
Pegasus Tours, 458-3049
Internet Café, Vieux Fort, 454-7722

Medical Facilities and Emergency Numbers

Customs:
Castries, 452-3487
Marigot, 451-4257
Rodney Bay, 452-0235
Vieux Fort, 454-6565
Marine Police: 452-2595, VHF: 16
Emergency: 99
Air/Sea Rescue: 452-2894
Hospitals:
Victoria, 453-7059
St. Jude's Vieux Fort 454-6041
Soufriere, 459-7258
Dennery, 453-3310

For more information on St. Lucia, please refer to Chris Doyle's **Sailor's Guide to the Windward Islands**. Contact Cruising Guide Publications at 800-330-9542 or www.cruisingguides.com.

Directory of Marinas & Services

Windward Islands: Saint Lucia

Jalousie Cove Marina	758-459-7666
Marigot Bay Resort and Marina/ The Moorings	758-451-4357
Rodney Bay Boatyard and Marina	758-452-8215
St. Lucia Yacht Services, Castries	758-452-5057
Waterside Landings, Rodney Bay	758-452-5241

Directory of Boatyards & Services

Windward Islands: Saint Lucia

Castries Yacht Center	758-452-6234
Rodney Bay Boatyard and Marina	758-452-8215

Carenantilles

MARTINIQUE www.carenantilles.com

Baie des Tourelles - 97200 Fort de France :

Tel. : 0596 63 76 74 - Fax : 0596 71 66 83 - E-mail : carenfdf@sasi.fr

Crane 35 T - Forklift 12 T - 140 spaces - LONG TERM STORAGE.
Water, electricity (220v / 380v), fuel, trailers for storage, fax, telephone, bathroom facilities,
bar - restaurant. CERTIFIED PARTNER OF THE SOCIETE ANTILLAISE D'EXPERTISE.

CADET-PETIT Electricity, winding, alternators, starters	Mob : 0596 23 67 75	**POLYMAR** Construction & repair, paint, fiberglass	Tel : 0596 70 62 88 Fax : 0596 60 10 97
CARAIBES BOAT SERVICES Fuel, water, cold drinks, ice, gas Fishing equipment - store open 7 days a week	Tel : 0596 71 73 91 Fax : 0596 71 73 96	**ROLLAND Jean-Michel** Stainless steel & aluminum welding, boilerwork, tubing	Tel : 0596 71 49 28 Fax : 0596 71 95 74
CHALMESSIN Aluminum and stainless steel welding	Tel : 0596 60 03 79 Tel : 0596 60 03 75 Fax : 0596 63 49 67	**SCUBA TECH** Scubadiving & harpooning equipment Filling & retesting station	Tel : 0596 72 86 84 Fax : 0596 72 86 85
COOPEMAR Fishing tackle and equipment & life rafts - navigation electronics Emergency beacon & survival equipment customer service	Tel : 0596 73 37 54 Tel : 0596 63 68 49 Fax : 0596 63 76 63	**BISTROT DU PORT** Bar - Restaurant	Tel : 0596 60 27 65
MANU VOILES Textile manufacture & sail repair	Tel : 0596 63 10 61 Fax : 0596 63 65 23	**STATION DE PILOTAGE** Pilotage - boatage	Tel : 0596 63 20 88 Fax : 0596 63 81 90
MER & SPORT Nautical and fishing equipment, fittings	Tel : 0596 71 19 20	**YAVE MARINE / EURO NAUTIC** Mercury, Mercruiser, Mariner (H.B./I.B) customer service	Mob : 0696 45 68 55 Fax : 0596 56 92 53
NAUTIC-BOIS Fittings, wood and epoxy repair, framework	Tel : 0596 71 82 33 Fax : 0596 71 95 74		
PLUS NAUTIQUE - MERCURY MARTINIQUE Nautical equipment & fittings Dealer Mariner, Mercury, Bayliner, Wellcraft	Tel : 0596 63 75 49	**ALL TECHNICAL SERVICES**	

Old factory - 97290 Le Marin :

Tel : 0596 74 77 70 - Fax : 0596 74 78 22 - E-mail : carenmarin@sasi.fr

Crane 55 T - Dry-dock capacity 700 T / 16m long - Rolling cradle - 220 spaces.
Water, electricity (220v / 380v), fuel, cyber hull (internet access), fax, telephone, restroom facilities, bar - restaurant.

LONG TERM STORAGE - ALL TECHNICAL SERVICES

ANTILLES MARINE SERVICES Inboard motor sales and repair, spare parts	Tél. : 0596 74 70 78 Fax : 0596 74 63 71	**NAUTIC SERVICES** **& MARTINIQUE SUD SABLAGE** Dry-dock painting, sandblasting and dry blast cleaning	Tel : 0596 74 70 45 Mob : 0696 45 61 60 Fax : 0596 74 70 52
CARAIBES BOAT SERVICES Outboard motors, fuel, lubricant, water, gas, ice	Tel : 0596 74 70 30 Fax : 0596 74 70 31	**PLASTIC SERVICES** Paint stratification, fiberglass, osmosis treatment	Tel : 0596 74 70 37 Mob : 0696 25 07 69 Fax : 0596 74 70 43
CARENE SHOP Paint & cleaning products	Tel : 0596 74 74 80 Fax : 0596 74 79 16	**PLUS NAUTIQUE** Fittings & nautical material	Tel : 0596 74 62 12 Fax : 0596 74 62 22
DEGRAVE Alain Upkeep & maintenance	Mob : 0696 84 24 12	**SUD MARINE ELECTRONIQUE** Marine electronics & electricity	Tel : 0596 74 65 56 Mob : 0696 45 68 04 Fax : 0596 74 69 54
LA CARENE Bar - restaurant	Mob : 0696 91 51 76	**TILIKUM** Marine refrigeration	Tel : 0596 74 67 03 Mob : 0696 22 79 89 Fax : 0596 74 66 63
LA SURVY Fittings & nautical material	Tel : 0596 74 63 03 Fax : 0596 74 63 00	**TOUR DE FRAISE** Belaying cleats, countersinking, aluminum & stainless steel welding	Tel : 0596 74 85 65 Fax : same Mob : 0696 28 44 78
LES AS TECK Marine carpentry	Tel : 0596 74 72 85 Fax : same	**VOILERIE ASSISTANCE** Production & repair	Tel : 0596 74 88 32 Mob : 0596 45 40 48
NAUTIC & CO Marine mechanics, certified MITSUBISHI dealer	Tel : 0596 74 66 73 Mob : 0696 26 11 82 Fax : 0596 74 72 72		

SOCIETE ANTILLAISE D'EXPLOITATION DE PORTS DE PLAISANCE

PORT DE PLAISANCE DU MARIN

Port Office - (de 8:30 - 12:30 & 14:00 à 18:00)
Bd Allègre - Bassin Tortue - 97290 Le Marin
Tel. : (+596) 596 74 83 83 - Fax : (+596) 596 74 92 20 - VHF Canal 9
Web site : www.portmarin.com - E-mail : port.marin@wanadoo.fr

Services & facilities

Telephone, fax, photocopying • Laundry
"TOTAL" marine fueling station : fuel and lubricants
Restroom facilities • Taxis • Car rental

Pict. Pierre COURTINARD

| 600 berths | 2 500 m² area for vessels | 40 mooring buoys |

Professionals

Boat rental (14 companies)
Fittings - Rigging
Sail loft
Mechanics - Electronics
Fishing - Diving Club

Businesses

Bar • Restaurants
Provisioning
ATM
Shops

St. Vincent and the Grenadines

Culture

St. Vincent is a beautiful yet atypical island for the West Indies. Highly mountainous in structure and lacking in beaches and resorts, St. Vincent doesn't cater to the normal tourism that the rest of the Caribbean offers. Instead, however, St. Vincent offers natural beauty including Soufriere, St. Vincent's dormant volcano, which dominates the northern end of the island at a dramatic height of 3,000 feet. These mountainous regions are lush with green forest and foliage and are also home to beautiful botanical gardens and an amazing variety of wildlife. However, the characteristic Caribbean features such as white sand beaches, resorts etc. can be found on the Grenadines, a group of smaller islands that stretch between St. Vincent to the north and Grenada to the south. What St. Vincent lacks, the Grenadines make up for and vice versa. This plus the proximity of the islands of the Grenadines to each other makes for fabulous cruising and day sails. The Grenadines include 32 islands and cays, the main islands of which are Bequia, Canouan, Mustique, Palm Island, Petite St. Vincent, Mayreau and Union Island.

Whereas the Europeans discovered and conquered most of the Caribbean islands, St. Vincent remained somewhat uncivilized for quite a few more years than the others. Originally exclusively Arawak, St. Vincent would soon become overrun by Carib Indians. Most of the present-day natives of St. Vincent are in some capacity descendants of the Caribs, though at some point when a ship carrying slaves from Africa wrecked off the coast of Bequia, the Africans and Caribs would intermarry, thereby becoming the "Black Caribs". St. Vincent remained British for the most part until the island gained independence in 1979. St. Vincent is predominantly English speaking.

Currency

St. Vincent's form of currency is the EC (Eastern Caribbean) dollar. Major credit cards are widely accepted as well.

Customs and Immigration

Ports of Entry are the following:

St. Vincent: Wallilabou, Kingstown, 8am-12pm, 1pm-4pm, overtime incurs fees

Bequia: Port Elizabeth, weekdays 8:30-6pm (overtime is after 4pm), Saturdays 8:30am-12pm, and 3pm-6pm (afternoon is overtime)

Union Island: Clifton, 8:30am-6pm, immigration is at the airport

There is a $10EC entry charge per person and a $2EC charge per foot per month for yachts on charter.

Airline Access

Air Caraibes	Air Martinique
American Eagle	BWIA Express
Caribbean Star	LIAT

Mustique Airways, SVG, Grenada Air, and TIA are all charter airlines.

Communications

St. Vincent and the Grenadines' calling system is like that of the U.S. with an area code of 784 and a 7-digit local number. St. Vincent and the Grenadines all have the same area code.

Calling St. Vincent and the Grenadines from another country:
from the U.S., dial 1 + 784 + 7-digit local number
from the U.K., dial 00 + 1 + 784 + 7-digit local number
Calling another country from St. Vincent and the Grenadines:
to the U.S., dial 1 + area code and 7-digit local number
to the U.K., dial 011 + 44 + city code and local number
Calling within St. Vincent and the Grenadines:
dial the 7-digit local number
International operator: 115

Card and coin phones are available all over the island as well as Bequia and Mustique. Phone cards are available for purchase at Post Offices and selected shops. They are also on Bequia and Mustique.

Internet Cafés:
Iconet, Bequia
Gingerbread, Bequia, 458-3800
RMS, Bequia, 458-4556

Medical Facilities and Emergency Numbers

St. Vincent
Botanic Clinic: 457-9781
Customs: 456-1083
Emergency (fire, police, and medical): 999
Maryfield Hospital: 457-8991/1300
Police: 456-1185

Bequia
Police: 458-3211
Customs: 457-3044
Imperial Pharmacy: 458-3373
Bequia Hospital: VHF 74
Union Island
Customs: 458-8360
Health Center: 458-8339

For more information on St. Vincent and the Grenadines, please refer to Chris Doyle's **Sailor's Guide to the Windward Islands**. Contact Cruising Guide Publications at 800-330-9542 or www.cruisingguides.com.

Tourist Office: St. Vincent, 784-457-1502/1957

Directory of Marinas & Services

Windward Islands: Bequia
Bequia Marina, Admiralty Bay   784-458-3246

Windward Islands: St. Vincent
Barefoot Yacht Charters   784-456-9526
The Lagoon   784-458-4308
Ottley Hall   784-457-2178

Windward Islands: Union Island
Anchorage Yacht Club, Clifton Harbour   784-458-8221
Bouganvillia Marine Mall, Clifton Harbour   784-458-8878

Windward Islands: Petite Martinique
B & C Fuels   473-443-9110

J. Raycroft

Directory of Boatyards & Services

Windward Islands: Bequia
Bequia Slip, Admiralty Bay   784-458-3272

Windward Islands: St. Vincent
Ottley Hall   784-457-2178

Grenada and Carriacou

Culture

Grenada is a particularly beautiful island containing a green mountainous interior, beaches, palms, resorts and an exceptional flowering season. Nicknamed the "Isle of Spice" because of the abundance of such spices as nutmeg, cinnamon, bay leaf, allspice, and ginger, the independent nation of Grenada also includes Carriacou and Petite Martinique. Carriacou, a small island only 8 miles long and 5 miles wide, is as yet unspoiled by tourism; a perfect getaway from everything, even civilization.

Though Grenada was discovered by Columbus in the late 15th century, the Caribs, who had lived there for centuries having succeeded the Arawaks, would continue to live on Grenada for another 150 years. The French took control of the island in 1672 and retained control for nearly a century until 1762 when British forces invaded. In 1877, Grenada became a crown colony and gained full independence in 1974. In the last several years, Grenada has been experiencing a growth period and in addition, has instated national park areas for the protection of the rain forests and coral reefs, making the wildlife exceptionally beautiful.

The language spoken is English.

Currency

The currency used in Grenada and Carriacou is the EC (Eastern Caribbean) dollar. Major credit cards are accepted at large establishments as are traveler's checks.

Customs and Immigration

Ports of Entry are the following:
Grenada: St. George's, Prickley Bay
               Mt. Hartman Bay, and St. David's Harbour
Carriacou: Hillsborough

Hours are weekdays, 8am-11:45am, 1pm-3:45pm. Other hours incur an overtime fee.

Port entry fees are $45EC-$70EC depending on vessel size, and $5U.S. per person. It is necessary to check with customs the port authority and immigration, and 4 copies of a crew list will be needed.

Airline Access

Air Jamaica	American Airlines
American Eagle	British Airways
BWIA	Caribbean Star
Condor	LIAT
Monarch Airlines	
St. Vincent & the Grenadines Air (SVG Air)	

Communications

Grenada and Carriacou work like the U.S., both having an area code of 473 and a 7-digit local number.

Calling Grenada and Carriacou from another country:
from the U.S., dial 1 + 473 + 7-digit local number
from the U.K., dial 00 + 1 + 473 + 7-digit local number
Calling another country from Grenada and Carriacou:
to the U.S., dial 1 + area code + 7-digit local number
to the U.K., dial 011 + 44 + city code and local number
Calling within Grenada and Carriacou:
dial 7-digit local number

Card and coin phones can be found everywhere. Cards can be purchased in Post Offices and selected shops.
Internet Cafés:
Grenada:
        Boatyard Restaurant and Tiki Bar, 444-4662
        Carenge Café, 440-8701
        Onsite Software Support, 444-3653
Carriacou:
        Carriacou Yacht Club, 443-6292
        The Seablast, 443-6602

Medical Facilities and Emergency Numbers

Grenada
    Customs:
        Prickley Bay, 444-4509
        St. George's, 440-2239/2240
    Coast Guard: 399
    Police: 911
    Emergency Hospital: 434
    Port Authority: 444-4101, VHF 16

Carriacou
  Customs: 443-7659
  Hospital Emergency: 774

For more information on Grenada and Carriacou please refer to Chris Doyle's **Sailor's Guide to the Windward Islands**. Contact Cruising Guide Publications at 800-330-9542 or www.cruisingguides.com.

Tourist Office: Grenada Hotel and Tourism Association Ltd., St. George's, 1-473-444-1353

Directory of Marinas & Services
Windward Islands: Carriacou
Tyrrel Bay Yacht Haul-out 473-443-8175

Windward Islands: Grenada
Clarkes Court Bay Marina 473-439-2593

Grenada Marine, St. David's Harbour
(See our ad on p. 102) 473-443-1667
Grenada Yacht Club, St. George's 473-440-3050
Grenada Yacht Services, St. George's 473-440-2508
Island Water World, St. George's
(See our ad on the outside back cover) 473-435-2150
Moorings Secret Harbour, Mt. Hartman Bay 473-444-4449
**Spice Island Marine Services Ltd.,
Prickly Bay** *(See our ad on p. 100)* 473-444-4257
True Blue Bay 473-443-8783

Directory of Boatyards & Services
Windward Islands: Carriacou
Tyrrel Bay Yacht Haul-out 473-443-8175

Windward Islands: Grenada
Grenada Marine, St. David's Harbour 473-443-1667
**Spice Island Marine Services Ltd.,
Prickly Bay** *(See our ad on p. 100)* 473-444-4257

St. Georges Harbour, Grenada

J. Raycroft

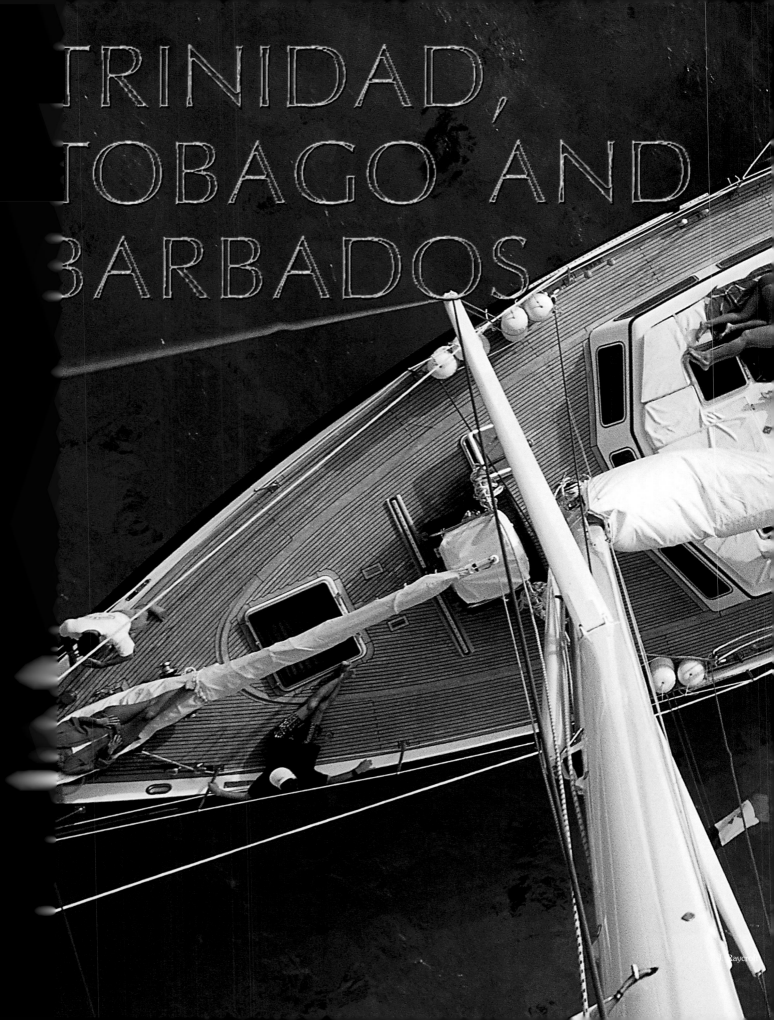

TRINIDAD, TOBAGO AND BARBADOS

PORT DE PLAISANCE DU MARIN

SOCIÉTÉ ANTILLAISE D'EXPLOITATION DE PORT DE PLAISANCE

Port Office - (de 8:30 à 12:30 & 14:00 à 18:00)
Bd Allègre – Bassin Tortue – 97290 Le Marin
Tel. : (+596) 596 74 83 83 - Fax : (+596) 596 74 92 20 - VHF Canal 9
Web site : www.portmarin.com - e-mail : port.marin@wanadoo.fr

Services & facilities

Telephone, fax, photocopying • Laundry
TOTAL marine fueling station : fuel and lubricants
Restroom facilities • Taxis • Car rental

The Southernmost Islands in the Eastern Caribbean
Provide Refuge from Hurricanes

Trinidad & Tobago

Culture

Trinidad and Tobago has had a resurgence of interest for the yachting community in the past few years. For many years, the islands were considered too far away with little or nothing for which to visit. However, now the country has become one of the best areas for yacht services and repair in the Lesser Antilles with the marine industry based in Chaguaramas National Park, Trinidad. The government has made a concerted effort to increase the number of haul-out and service facilities and to train individuals for the marine industry, thereby making Trinidad the definitive marine service center with hundreds of haul-out and service facilities all over the island. Though Trinidad is highly industrialized, there is no lack of culture here. In fact, not only is Carnival here considered one of the finest in the world, many people actually plan their vacations in order to be in Trinidad and Tobago during Carnival time. Trinidad and Tobago is also the origin of steel pan and calypso music.

Tobago offers a typically Caribbean atmosphere of relaxation and calm. It also offers palmed and sandy shores and a lush and verdant interior. An exciting array of flora and fauna can be found that belong to this island alone. Tobago is also considered to be a premium diving spot. Trinidad is different on several main points.

Where Tobago is relaxed and quiet, Trinidad is more cosmopolitan. Also, Trinidad lacks the typical Caribbean island appeal. Instead, her geography has been likened to that of South America with forest and swamp, many birds, manatees and turtles.

Culturally, art galleries, theaters, museums and restaurants allow a variety of things to do.

Whilst Trinidad was discovered by Columbus and later colonized by Spain, Tobago wasn't colonized until 1632 by the Dutch. Trinidad would become English in 1797, Tobago also becoming English and then French. In 1888 both islands were finally united and joined the West Indies Federation. In 1958 but became independent in 1962 under the commonwealth and in August of 1976, Trinidad and Tobago became a republic. The islands are both English speaking.

Currency

The country of Trinidad and Tobago uses the TT dollar that varies in value to the U.S. dollar. Currently, the exchange rate is roughly 6TT to $1U.S. However, the U.S. dollar is widely used. Credit cards and travelers checks are generally accepted.

Customs and Immigration

Trinidad: Port of entry in Trinidad is Chaguaramas where someone is on duty 24 hours a day

600 berths 2 500 m² area for vessels 40 mooring buoys

Professionals

Boat rental (14 companies)
Fittings - Rigging
Sail loft
Fishing - Diving Club

Businesses
Restaurants
Provisioning
ATM
Shops

Port St. Charles

Bridgetown

BARBADOS

Charlotteville

TOBAGO

Scarborough

Chaguaramas

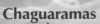

GULF OF PARIA

TRINIDAD

Not to scale.

Port St. Charles, Barbados

Courtesy of Port St. Charles

Ports of Entry

Trinidad:
Chaguaramas

Tobago:
Scarborough
Charlotteville

Barbados:
Bridgetown
Port St. Charles

Aerial of Grand Fond Bay, Trinidad   J. Fisher, _Cruising Guide to Trinidad and Tobago_

Carenantilles

Airline Access

Air Canada	
American Airlines	
ALM Antillean Airlines	
American Eagle	
BWIA International	
Caledonian Airways	
Guyana Airways	
LIAT	
Suriname Airways	
Caribbean Star	

Charter Airlines:

American TransAir, Aserca Airlines, Avior Technologies Inc., Condor Airlines, Carnival Air, Sun Country Airlines

Communications

The Trinidad and Tobago phone system works like the U.S. with an area code of 868.

Calling Trinidad and Tobago from another country:
- from the U.S., dial 1 + 868 + 7-digit local number
- from the U.K., dial 00 + 1 + 868 + 7-digit local number

Calling another country from Trinidad and Tobago:
- to the U.S., dial 1 + area code + 7-digit local number
- to the U.K., dial 011 + 44 + city code and local number

Within Trinidad and Tobago:
- dial 7-digit local number

Public card phones are available on both islands and cards are available for purchase in Trinidad at marinas and clubs. In Port of Spain, they can be purchased at the TSTT (Telecommunications Services Trinidad and Tobago). You may also purchase phone cards at banks, the TSTT building, post offices and other select shops.

Operator: 0
Local directory assistance: 6211
International directory assistance: 0

Internet Cafés:

Trinidad:
Island Surf Café, 634-2407
Ocean Internet Café, 634-2233/1205
The Mariner's Office Ltd., 634-4183
ITC CyberCafe, 632-7269
Cybertrini Internet Café, 655-6650
Browwwser's CyberCafé, 653-4663
The Internet Café, 657-8692
Trinicaf Cyber Café, 678-5523
Same but Different Communications, 634-1360
Solutions.com, 657-6448
Webyss Services Ltd., 752-6640
Cell-U-Tech Communications, 628-1889

Tobago:
Blue Waters Inn, 660-2583
CyberCafé, 639-0007
Matrix Technology, 639-4220
Jessie Tech (Scarborough)
Shenda's Email (Charlotteville)

Medical Facilities and Emergency Numbers

Trinidad:
Coast Guard: 634-4440
Customs: 625-3341
Fire/Ambulance: 990
Rapid Response: 999
Emergency Health Service: 653-4343
Police: 999
General Hospital: 623-2951/2952

Tobago:
Customs: 639-2415
Ambulance: 639-2108
General Hospital: 639-2551
Coast Guard: 265-4939
Police: 639-1200
Emergency Health Service: 653-4444

For more information on Trinidad and Tobago, please refer to Chris Doyle's *Cruising Guide to Trinidad and Tobago Plus Barbados*. Contact Cruising Guide Publications at 800-330-9542 or www.cruisingguides.com.

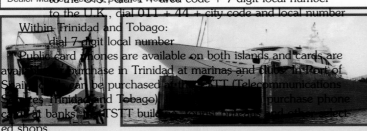

Directory listings

CADET-PETIT — Electricity, welding, alternators, starters	Mob : 0596 23 67 75
CARAIBES BOAT SERVICES — Fuel, water, cold drink, ice, Fishing equipment, open 7 days a week	
CHALMESSIN — Aluminum and stainless steel welding	Tel : 0596 60 03 79 / Tel : 0596 60 03 75 / Fax : 0596 63 49 67
COOPEMAR — Fishing tackle and equipment & life rafts, navigation electronics, Emergency beacon & survival equipment	Tel : 0596 73 37 54 / Tel : 0596 63 68 49 / Fax : 0596 63 76 63
MANU VOILES — Textile manufacture & sail repair	Tel : 0596 63 10 61 / Fax : 0596 63 65 23
MER & SPORT — Marine and fishing equipment fittings	Tel : 0596 71 19 20
NAUTIC-BOIS — Fittings, wood and epoxy repair framework	Tel : 0596 71 82 33 / Fax : 0596 71 95 74
PLUS NAUTIQUE — MERCURY MARTINIQUE — Nautical equipment, Dealer Mariner-Mercury	Tel : 0596 63 75 49
POLYMAR — Construction & repair	Tel : 0596 70 62 88 / Fax : 0596 60 10 97
ROLLAND Jean-Michel — Stainless steel	Tel : 0596 71 49 28 / Fax : 0596 71 95 74
SCUBA TECH — Scubadiving, Filling & retailing station	Tel : 0596 72 86 84 / Fax : 0596 72 86 85
BISTROT DU PORT — Bar - Restaurant	Tel : 0596 60 27 65
STATION DE PILOTAGE — Pilotage - bateaux	Tel : 0596 63 65 88 / Fax : 0596 63 65 90
YAVE MARINE / EURO NAUTIC — Mercury, Mercruiser, Mariner (H.B./I.B) customer service	Mob : 0696 45 68 55
ANTILLES MARINE SERVICES — Inboard motor sales and spares	Tél : 0596 74 70 78 / Fax : 0596 74 63 71
CARAIBES BOAT SERVICES — Outboard motors, fuel, forecast, water, gas	Tel : 0596 74 70 30 / Fax : 0596 74 70 31
CARENE SHOP — Paint & cleaning products	Tel : 0596 74 74 80 / Fax : 0596 74 79 16
DEGRAVE Alain — Upkeep & maintenance	Mob : 0696 84 24 12
LA CARENE — Bar - restaurant	Mob : 0696 91 51 76
LA SURVY — Fittings & nautical material	Tel : 0596 74 63 03 / Fax : 0596 74 63 00
LES AS TECK — Marine carpentry	Tel : 0596 74 72 85 / Tel : same
NAUTIC & CO — Marine mechanics, certified MITSUBISHI dealer	Tel : 0596 74 66 73 / Mob : 0696 26 11 82 / Fax : 0596 74 72 72
NAUTIC SERVICES & MARTINIQUE SUD SABLAGE — Dry-dock painting, sandblasting and dry blast cleaning	Tel : 0596 74 70 45 / Mob : 0696 45 61 60 / Fax : 0596 74 70 52
PLASTIC SERVICES — Paint stratification, fiberglass, osmosis treatment	Tel : 0596 74 70 37 / Mob : 0696 25 07 69 / Fax : 0596 74 70 43
PLUS NAUTIQUE — Fittings & nautical material	Tel : 0596 74 62 12 / Fax : 0596 74 62 22
SUD MARINE ELECTRONIQUE — Marine electronics & electricity	Tel : 0596 74 65 56 / Mob : 0696 45 68 04 / Fax : 0596 74 69 54
TILIKUM — Marine refrigeration	Tel : 0596 74 67 03 / Mob : 0696 22 79 89
TOUR DE FRAISE — Belaying cleats, counter-sinking, stainless steel welding	Tel : 0596 74 66 63 / Mob : 0596 74 85 55
VOILERIE ASSISTANCE — Production & repair	Tel : 0596 74 88 32 / Mob : 0596 45 40 48

Tourism Offices: Trinidad, 868-623-6022/3, Tobago, 868-639-2125

Carriacou Customs: 443-7659

Hospital Emergency: 774

Barbados

For more information on Grenada and Carriacou please refer to Chris Doyle's *Sailor's Guide to the Windward Islands*. Contact Cruising Guide Publications at 800-330-9542 or www.cruisingguides.com

Barbados is the most easterly of all the Caribbean islands, situated 200 miles NNE of Trinidad, almost as far east as Greenland. This island is atypical on many counts. Named by the Portuguese that discovered her in the 15th century, Barbados means "the bearded ones" for the many bearded fig trees found on the isle. The first and last settlers were the British, unlike many of the Caribbean islands whose histories of ownership and capture are long and involved to say the least. In 1966 Barbados became independent and is now a sovereign state in the British Commonwealth.

Although Barbados is only 166 square miles in area, in contrast the island's population is 265,000, one of the most densely populated islands in the Caribbean. Barbados is a very cosmopolitan island for the Caribbean, whose sole income is tourism. The island is thus covered with resorts. If you are a nature-lover, much more offering many activities for a reasonable price. Nevertheless, the natives are friendly and there is wildlife in the anchorages.

The Barbados dollar is the official currency and is pegged to the U.S. dollar at a rate of $1 U.S. to 2 Barbados dollars. Major credit cards are widely accepted.

There are two ports of entry in Barbados, Bridgetown and Port St. Charles. There is an agreement that states that you must clear in and out at the same port. When entering Bridgetown contact the Signal Station on VHF 16 or 68 for instructions. In Port St. Charles, contact the dock master or customs directly at VHF 16 or 77. Stay aboard until they come to you. Fees include $25 Barbados to clear in, $25 Barbados to clear out, and $8.33 Barbados anchoring fee. Overtime starts at 10pm and is extra.

Directory of Marinas & Services

Windward Islands: Carriacou
Tyrrel Bay Yacht Haul-out — 473-443-8175

Windward Islands: Grenada
Clarkes Court Bay Marina — 473-439-2593

Airline Access

Grenada Marine, St. David's Harbour
(See our ad on p. 202)
Grenada Yacht Club, St. George's
Grenada British Airways, St. George's
Island Water World, St. George's
(See our ad on the inside back cover)
Moorings Sea Tech Harbour, Mt. Hartman Bay
Spice Island Marine Services Ltd.,
Prickly Bay *(See our ad on p. 99)*
True Blue Bay

Air Canada	
Air Martinique	
British Airways	
CariWorld	
US Airways	
Air 2000/Air Tours PLC	
Caledonian Airways	
Key Airlines Inc.	

Air Jamaica — 473-443-1667
American Airlines — 473-440-3050
BWIA — 473-440-2508
LIAT
Charter: — 473-435-2150
Britannia Airways — 473-444-4449
Canadian Airlines Int.
— 473-444-4257

Communications

Barbados Boatyards & Services: 246

To call Barbados from another country:
from the U.S. dial 1 + 246 + 7-digit local number
from the U.K. dial 00 + 1 + 246 + 7-digit local number

To call another country from Barbados:
to the U.S., dial 1 + area code + 7-digit local number
to the U.K. dial 011 + 44 + city code and local number
Within Barbados:
dial 7-digit local number.

Card phones are available around the island. Cards can be purchased... Internet Access, 431-0756

Medical Facilities and Emergency Numbers

Customs: 430-2306
Immigration: 426-1011
Health Offices: 426-5080
Coast Guard: 436-6185
Port Authority: 434-4700

Fire: 311
Ambulance: 511

For more information on Barbados, please refer to Chris Doyle's *Cruising Guide to Trinidad and Tobago Plus Barbados*. Contact Cruising Guide Publications at 800-330-9542 or www.cruisingguides.com

Barbados Tourist Office: 888-427-2623

J. Raycroft

Directory of Marinas & Services

Trinidad

Bay View Marina, Gaspar Grande   868-678-9001

Crews Inn Marina,
Chaguaramas Bay *(See our ad on p. 108)*   868-634-4384

Coral Cove Marina,
Chaguaramas Bay *(See our ad on p. 110)*   868-634-2040

Peake Yacht Services,
Chaguarams Bay *(See our ad on the inside front cover)* 868-634-4427

Power Boat Mutual Facilities Ltd,
Chaguaramas Bay   868-634-4303

Tardieu Marine, Chaguaramas Bay   868-634-4534

Trinidad and Tobago Sailing Association,
Carenage Bay   868-634-4210

Tropical Marine, Chaguaramas Bay   868-634-4502

Barbados

Barbados Sailing and Cruising Club, Carlisle Bay   246-426-4434

Barbados Yacht Club, Carlisle Bay   246-427-1125

The Boatyard, Carlisle Bay   246-436-2622

Port St. Charles Marina   246-419-1000

Directory of Boatyards & Services

Trinidad

Crews Inn Marina,
Chaguaramas Bay *(See our ad on p. 108)*   868-634-4384

Coral Cove Marina,
Chaguaramas Bay *(See our ad on p. 110)*   868-634-2040

I.M.S. Yacht Services, Chaguaramas Bay   868-625-2104

Peake Yacht Services,
Chaguarams Bay *(See our ad on the inside front cover)* 868-634-4427

Power Boat Mutual Facilities Ltd,
Chaguaramas Bay   868-634-4303

Trinidad and Tobago Sailing Association,
Carenage Bay   868-634-4210

Barbados

The Boatyard, Carlisle Bay   246-436-2622

Grenada Marine
Full Service ... yard 12°N

... 32ft beam Travelift
... larger catamarans
Fibreglass/Gelcoat Repairs
Awl Grip Paint Jobs
Bottom Painting ...
Rigging & Ca...
Metalwork Sho...
Marine Engineer...
Plastic Boat Covering...

Customs & Immigration
Internet Cafe
Laundry & Shower Facilities
Mail and Parcel Drop-off & Pick-up
24 hour Security/Fenced Yard

Island Water World
Marine Chandlery

Shipwrights Ltd
Wooden Yacht Specialists

G. M Beach ...
West Indian Flavours ...

P. O/ Box ...
Tel: 473-44... ...052
info@grenadama...

... Boatyards
... Islands, Bequ...
Bequia Slip, Admiralty Ba...
... St. Vincent

... and Carriacou

Grenada is a particularly beaut...
mountainous interior, beaches, palms, reso...
stormy season. Nicknamed the Isl...
... such spices as nutmeg, cinnamon, bay...
... ginger. ... Grenada also...
Carriacou ... Carriacou ...
... miles long and 5 miles wide, is as yet unspoiled by tourism; a
perfect getaway ... even civilization.

Though Grenada was discovered by Columbus ...
... the Caribs, who had ... here for centuries ...
... Arawaks, would ... on Grenada ...
... years. The French took control of the island in ...
... century until 173...

The language spoken ... English.

Currency

The currency used ... Grenada and Carriacou is the EC
(Eastern Caribbean) dollar. Major credit cards are accepted at large
establishments as are traveler's checks.

Customs ... Immigration

... of Entry are the following:
... St. George's, Prickley Bay
... Mt. Hartman Bay, and St. David's Harbour
Carriacou ... Hillsborough
... hours are weekdays, 8am-11:45am, 1pm-3:45pm. Other
... incur an overtime fee.
... entry fees are $45EC-$70EC depending on vessel size,
... $5U.S. per person. It is necessary to check with customs the
... authority and immigration and 4 copies of a crew list will be
needed.

Airline A...

... ...ican Airlines
... ...sh Airways
... ...an Star
... ...s Air (SVG Air)

Communications

Grenada and Carriacou ... the U.S., both having an area
code of 473 and a 7-digit local number
Calling Grenada ... Carriacou from another country:
... from the ... ...digit local number
... + 7-digit local number
Calling ... out ... and Carriacou:
... S. ... ...digit local number
... + ...de and local number
... and Ca...

Carriacou ... ph... ... everywhere. Cards can be
purchased ... Post Office ... ...ed shops

... Internet ...
... Grenada...
... B... ...restaurant and Tiki Bar, 444-4662
Caree... ...: 440-8701
Onsite Solut... ...support 444-3653
Carriacou:
Carriacou Yacht Club, 443-6292
The Seablast, 443-6602

Medical Facilities and Emergency Numbers
Grenada
Customs:
Prickley Bay: 444-4509
St. George's, 440-2239/2240
Coast Guard: 399
... 911
Emergency Hospital: 434
... Authority: 444-4101, VHF 16

J. Raycroft

ARUBA, BONAIRE CURAÇAO

Three Islands with Three Personalities and One Culture

The ABC's include Aruba, Bonaire and Curaçao and are located at the bottom of the island chain directly above Venezuela. Both Bonaire and Curaçao are part of the Netherlands Antilles whereas Aruba, having separated from the Netherlands Antilles is now an independent nation. While each island has its own charm and distinct character, all three of the ABC's are connected by a common culture that results in beautiful Dutch colonial architecture spread across all three islands. A shared language exclusive to the ABC's called Papiamento is a testament to the many cultural influences the islands have had over the course of their histories, as it appears to be a melange of Spanish, Dutch, Portuguese, English, French, and African. The people are mostly a mix of Arawak, African slave, Dutch and Spanish and are reputed to be extremely kind and welcoming. Aside from cultural highlights, the ABC's are renowned for beautiful waters, excellent diving, beaches and hillsides. Whilst all islands are certainly yacht friendly, they are also extremely environment friendly, so make sure you are aware of the rules and regulations specific to each island. Check with Customs and Immigration when you clear in to find out specifics.

Aruba

Culture

Aruba is a 75 square mile island with 54,000 inhabitants and lots to do. Where Bonaire attracts the nature lovers and adventur-ers, Aruba attracts those interested in glitz and glam with an abundant night life, casinos, outdoor cafés, and fabulous hotels and resorts. Aruba is, however, still blessed with the natural beauty of white sandy beaches, and beautiful clear waters for diving and snorkeling. Aruba's nature is protected by a plan put in place by the government to make sure that, in the midst of growth in economy and tourism, her flora and fauna will remain yet unscathed.

Aruba was first inhabited by a sect of the Arawak tribe. In 1499, the island was discovered by westerners. The discoverer, however, has been disputed but assumed to be Alonso de Ojeda of Spain. Aruba was Spanish until the 1630's when the director of the Dutch West India Company claimed the island for the Dutch. Slowly, people of Europe, Curaçao, and Venezuela began to inhabit the island. Aruba remained Dutch, and in 1986 became a separate entity from the Netherlands Antilles within the Kingdom of the Netherlands. Today, languages spoken include Papiamento, Dutch, Spanish and English.

Currency

Aruba's form of currency is the Aruban Florin (also know as the Guilder). The exchange rate is 1.77 AFL to 1 US$, as the Florin fluctuates with the U.S. dollar on the market. Credit cards and traveler's checks are widely accepted, and ATM's are available, though only certain kinds of ATM cards can be used in Aruba. Check with 1-800-4-CIRRUS to see if yours will work. U.S. dollars are also commonly used and accepted.

ARUBA

Orenjestad

CURAÇAO

Willemstad

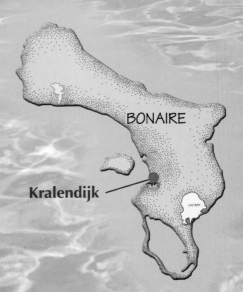

BONAIRE

Kralendijk

Not to scale.

Ports of Entry

Aruba:
Oranjestad

Bonaire:
Kralendijk

Curaçao:
Willemstad

J. Raycroft

Customs and Immigration

Aruba's Port of Entry is in Oranjestad in the commercial harbor. Contact the Aruban Port Authority on VHF 16 or 11 in order to find out where to tie up. There are no fees, and immigration will give 2 weeks with a possible 3-month extension.

Airline Access

The following is a list of most of the many airlines that fly directly or connect with flights that go to Aruba. Many of the airlines fly internationally from Europe, Canada, the United States, and many South and Central American countries.

ALM	American Airlines
American Eagle	British Airways
Continental	Delta
Dutch Caribbean Airways	KLM
Martinair	Royal Aruban Airlines
United Airlines	US Air

Communications

All Aruba's local 6-digit numbers begin with the number 8 (or 9 if the number is cellular).

Calling Aruba from another country:
> from the U.S., dial 011 + 297 + the 6-digit local number
> from the U.K., dial 00 + 297 + the 6-digit local number

Calling another country from Aruba:
> to the U.S., dial 00 + 1 + the area code and 7-digit local number
> to the U.K., dial 00 + 44 + city code and local number

Calling within Aruba: dial 6-digit local number

International Operator: 121

Pay phones are available around the island that use prepaid phone cards found in gas stations, retail stores and SETAR Teleshops.Cellular phone rentals are also available.

> Internet Café:
> Café Internet, Oranjestad, 824500

Medical Facilities and Emergency Numbers

> Police: 911
> Fire alarm/Hospital: 911
> Hospital and Ambulance: 874300
> Ambulance:
> > Oranjestad, 821234
> > San Nicolas, 845050
>
> Air Ambulance:
> > Richard Rupert, 829197, cellular, 93229
>
> Medical Center: 848833

For more information on Aruba, please refer to Susan Brushaber and Arnold Greenberg's **Aruba, Bonaire, and Curaçao Alive**. Contact Cruising Guide Publications at 800-330-9542 or www.cruisingguides.com.

> Tourist Office:
> Aruba Tourism Authority, Oranjestad, 823777

Bonaire

Culture

Bonaire is a quiet island whose main attractions lie in eco-touristic activities such as diving and bird watching (approximately two hundred species have been spotted). Due to heavy enforce-

J. Raycroft

ment of environmental protection by the government, Bonaire has been able to retain world-renowned clear waters and beautiful coral reef. The nearly 15,000 inhabitants of Bonaire are of mixed ancestry including Arawak, African, Dutch and Spanish. Bonaire's history is just as varied, beginning with the Arawaks who were the first to inhabit the island. In 1499, Bonaire was discovered by Italian Amerigo Vespuccio. In 1527, the island began to be colonized by the Spanish, an attempt that was abandoned over a century later. Soon after, the Dutch would arrive, officially making Bonaire a Dutch colony. With the exception of a brief British invasion in the 19th century, Bonaire has remained Dutch. Languages include Papiamento, Dutch, Spanish and English.

Currency

The currency in Bonaire is the Netherlands Antilles Florin (NAFL), also called the guilder. The NAFL fluctuates with the U.S. dollar on the world market, the exchange rate for which is approximately 1.77 NAFL for 1 U.S. dollar. The U.S. dollar is also widely accepted, as are travelers checks and major credit cards. There is an ATM at A.B.N. Bank that gives both U.S. dollars and guilders.

Customs and Immigration

The only Port of Clearance in Bonaire is in Kralendijk. There is no anchoring due to heightened environmental concern for the coral reefs, however there are many moorings provided by the Bonaire National Marine Park. You can either get a mooring or tie up to the north town pier near Customs. There are no fees at Customs and Immigration.

Airline Access

The following airlines have direct access to Bonaire from Europe, Latin America and the U.S. Other flights go through Curaçao.

Air Holland	ALM
American Airlines	American Eagle
Avensa	KLM
United Airlines	

Communications

All Bonaire numbers are 7-digits (717 + 4-digits).
Calling Bonaire from another country:
> from the U.S., dial 011 + 599 + 7-digit local number
> from the U.K., dial 00 + 599 + 7-digit local number

Calling another country from Bonaire:
> to the U.S., dial 00 + 1 + area code + 7-digit local number
> to the U.K., dial 00 + 44 + city code and local number

Calling within Bonaire:
> dial 7-digit local number.

USA Direct: 00-1-800-872-2881

The phone system in Bonaire is serviced by Telbo. A Telbo building can be found near the post office in Kralendijk, where collect calls, prepaid calls, and calls using USA direct can be made. Pay phones are available around the island. Cell phones can be hooked up with Telbo and other companies on the island.

Internet Cafés:
> DeTuin Internet Café and Restaurant, 599-717-2999
> Harbour Village Marina, 599-717-7419
> Gobey's Restaurant (connect laptop to a phone line and pay per minute), 599-717-8003
> BonaireLive, 599-717-6040
> Bonaire Public Library

Medical Facilities and Emergency Numbers

Ambulance/Police/Fire Department: 11
Hospital: 14

For more information on Bonaire, please refer to Chris Doyle's *Cruising Guide to Venezuela and Bonaire*, and Susan Brushaber and Arnold Greenberg's *Aruba, Bonaire, and Curaçao Alive*. Contact Cruising Guide Publications at 800-330-9542 or www.cruisingguides.com.
> Bonaire Tourist Office: 599-717-8322

Curaçao

Culture

Curaçao is the central island in the ABC group. The island is the most culturally influential of the three, being both the middle and largest of the island group. Curaçao's earliest known inhabitants were the Arawak Indians. The island was discovered then by a member of Christopher Columbus' fleet in 1499, but for the

most part was disregarded due to untenable land and a lack of fresh water. In the next several centuries, Curaçao would become the definitive slave-trading depot of the Caribbean. Strategically, Curaçao was a valuable port, and was thus fought over for several centuries by the French, Dutch, Spanish and English. In 1815, Curaçao finally became Dutch again under the Treaty of Paris, and in 1954 became the seat of the government for the newly autonomous Netherlands Antilles.

Much of Curaçao's past is still present in its Dutch colonial architecture in downtown Willemstad. And, with over 40 beaches, rolling hills, beautiful coral reefs and spectacular diving sites, Curaçao offers the best of both worlds, business and pleasure. Languages spoken include Papiamento, Dutch, Spanish and English.

Currency

The currency in Curaçao is the Netherlands Antilles Florin (NAFL), also called the guilder. The NAFL fluctuates with the U.S. dollar on the world market, the exchange rate for which is approximately 1.77 NAFL for 1 U.S. dollar. The U.S. dollar is also widely accepted, as are travelers checks and major credit cards. There are ATMs around the island.

Customs and Immigration

The only Port of Entry for Curaçao is Willemstad, where all government offices are located. Port officials can be contacted via VHF 16 or 12, using call sign "Fort Nassau". Contact them for instructions for docking, etc. at the fueling wharf of Sint Anna

Baai. A three-month stay is usually granted.

Airline Access

The following airlines service flights from the U.S., Europe, and Venezuela.

ALM	American Airlines
British Airways	KLM
Lufthansa	Servivensa
United Airlines	

Communications

Curaçao's area code and country code is 599-9 followed by a 7-digit local number.

Calling Curaçao from another country:
> from the U.S., dial 011 + 599-9 + 7-digit local number
> from the U.K., dial 00 + 599-9 + 7-digit local number

Calling another country from Curaçao:
> to the U.S., dial 00 + 1 + area code + 7-digit local number
> to the U.K., dial 00 + 44 + city code and local number

Calling within Curaçao:
> dial 7-digit local number

USA Direct: 001-800-872-2881

International Operator: 125

Phone system is sophisticated, and pay phones are located on the island.

Internet Cafés:
> Time Out Café, 667-2455

Bonaire

☑	Radio channel monitored: 16, 68	☐ Telephone hook-up: No
☐	Transient dockage:	☑ TV/cable: Yes
☐	Longterm dockage:	☑ Chandlery: Walking distance (Budget Marine)
☑	Anchoring near marina: Not allowed, only buoys	☑ Customs/Immigration: Walking distance
☐	Dockage rate:	☑ Hours: 8:00am - 5:00pm or by reservation
☐	Mooring rate:	
☑	Longest length: 90ft	☑ Currency/Credit Cards accepted: No credit cards accepted
☑	Catamaran dockage: Yes, one along side, slips max. 21ft wide	☑ Provisions: Walking distance (Super Markets)
☑	Depth at low water: 7ft	☑ Restaurant(s): Yes
☑	Electricity: 127v, 220v, 50hz	☑ Bars: Yes
☑	Water: Yes	☐ Computer access: No
☐	Fuel: No	☑ Marine Services: West Marine/Lewis Marine 2 days service
☐	Pump out station: No	
☐	Showers: No	
☑	Ice: Yes	

Yacht Service Association Curaçao
Spanish Water Curaçao Netherlands Antilles
Tel. no. 5999 7679042, 5999 7673014
E-mail kimakalk@bgate.net, sbmar@attglobal.net
www.yacht-service-curacao.com

Members	Tel no.	Website or E-mail
Seru Boca Marina	5999 7679042	www.santa-barbara-resort.com
Kima Kalki Marina	5999 7673014	www.kimakalkimarina.com
Curaçao Marine Services	5999 4658936	www.curacaomarine.com
Thomas Sails & Canvas	5999 7679015	thomas@bgate.net
Curaçao Yacht Club	5999 7674627	info@cyc.an
Sailmaker Rob Harms	5999 7369838	zeilroha@cura.net
Sarifundy's Marina	5999 7677643	sarifun@cura.net
Marine Technical Trading	5999 7673390	libergmt@carib-online.net
Stoffeerderij Antillana	5999 7671789	
Curaçao Yacht Services	5999 7363414	raaphorst@interneeds.net

Medical Facilities and Emergency Numbers

Ambulance: 112
Police: 911
Fire Department: 114
Hospital: 110

For more information on Curaçao, please refer to Susan Brushaber and Arnold Greenberg's *Aruba, Bonaire, and Curaçao Alive*. Contact Cruising Guide Publications at 800-330-9542 or www.cruisingguides.com.
Tourist Office: 461-6000, Willemstad

Directory of Marinas & Services

Aruba
Aruba Nautical Club, Spanish Lagoon   297-85-30-22
Bucuti Yacht Club, Oranjestad   297-82-37-93
Seaport Marina, Oranjestad   297-83-91-90

Bonaire
Bonaire Nautico Marina, Kralendijk
(See our ad on p. 118)   599-560-7254
Harbour Village Marina, Kralendijk   599-717-7500
Plaza Resort Marina, Kralendijk   599-717-2500

Curaçao
Curaçao Yacht Club, Brakkeput Ariba   599-9-767-4627
Kima Kalki Marina, Spanish Water   599-9-767-3014
Lions Dive Hotel and Marina, Willemstad   599-9-434-8888
Sarifundy's Marina, Spanish Water   599-9-767-7643

Port St. Charles   J. Fisher, *Cruising Guide to Trinidad and Tobago*

Seru Boca Marina, Spanish Water
(See our ad on p. 117)   599-9-767-9042

Directory of Boatyards & Services

Curaçao
Curaçao Marine Services   599-9-465-8936

VENEZUELA

J. Raycroft

This Magnificent Country offers the Opportunity to Visit Snow Covered Mountains, Dense Rainforests, and Tropical Islands

Culture

Venezuela is a country with many different facets. Between miles of rocky cliffs, tall mountains covered in snow, lush rainforest, waterfalls and miles of coastline, the scenery is all but mundane. This 352,143 square mile country contains a myriad of plants and animals to explore afloat and ashore. Venezuela is very boat-friendly, as there are many marinas and haul-out facilities, and you may leave your boat in storage for up to 18 months.

Columbus stepped onto Venezuela in 1498 as the first European to come to South America. As with many of the islands in the Caribbean, the Spanish would go on to exploit the native peoples into slavery, use them as slave labor, and ship them to other islands all over the Caribbean. It soon became obvious to the Spanish that Venezuela didn't house the same amount of mineral wealth as Peru and Mexico and they were thus quite slow to colonize the area. By the late 16th century, agriculture was booming and soon Venezuela would export cocoa, tobacco, and leather as their main economic activity.

Though Venezuela was recognized as a political entity as early as the late 18th century, it wasn't until the early 19th century that Venezuela would become independent from Spain. During the several centuries prior, Venezuela's political population would separate into two main groups, the conservatives and the liberals. Those who called themselves conservatives kept their loyalty to the government of the Spanish crown, not wanting the elite class to govern on principle, and those who called themselves liberals were pushing for self-government. These factions (with variations) would remain in place for the next 150 years, causing placement and replacement of despots, numerous coups, but also the emergence of liberators aiming to free Venezuela from Spanish control and to unite the world that was South America. Though Venezuela passed through varying political phases, the country remained a dictatorship for the most part until the mid 20th century when Romulo Bentacourt headed a revolt and succeeded in rewriting the Venezuelan constitution. Venezuela officially became a democracy under Bentacourt in 1959 when he was inaugurated as president. Since then, Venezuela has entered varying phases of economic and political instability. In the past 12 years, there have been two major coup attempts and uncertainty still remains. Luckily, the many years of war and rebellion have neither ravaged the natural beauty of the country nor disheartened the spirits of those who live there. Rather, Venezuelans are stronger for their histories and enriched by their backgrounds which in most cases is a mix of Indian, African, and European.

The official language of Venezuela is Spanish.

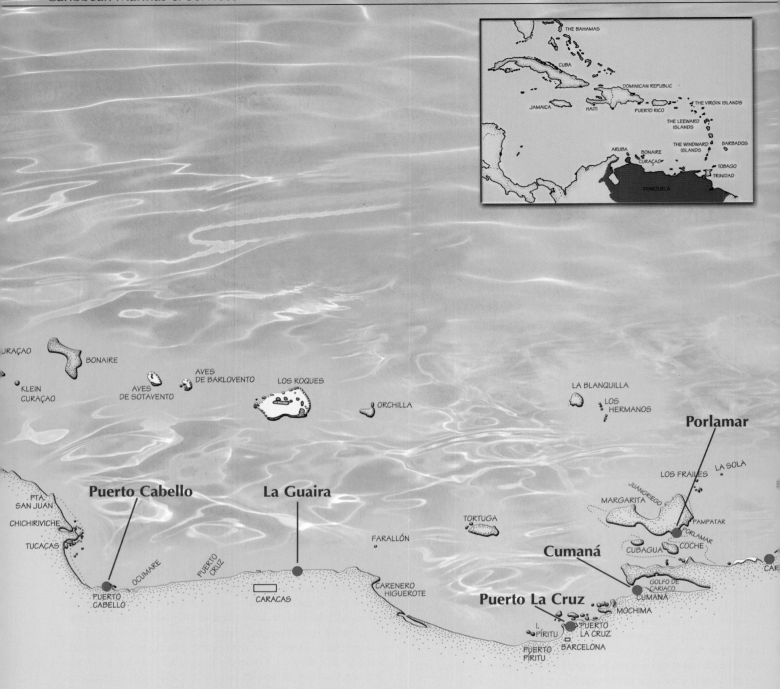

THE BAHAMAS

CUBA

JAMAICA

HAITI

DOMINICAN REPUBLIC

PUERTO RICO

THE VIRGIN ISLANDS

THE LEEWARD ISLANDS

THE WINDWARD ISLANDS

BARBADOS

ARUBA

BONAIRE

CURAÇAO

TOBAGO

TRINIDAD

VENEZUELA

CURAÇAO

BONAIRE

KLEIN CURAÇAO

AVES DE SOTAVENTO

AVES DE BARLOVENTO

LOS ROQUES

ORCHILLA

LA BLANQUILLA

LOS HERMANOS

Porlamar

LOS FRAILES

LA SOLA

JUANGRIEGO

MARGARITA

PAMPATAR

PORLAMAR

PTA. SAN JUAN

CHICHIRIVICHE

TUCACAS

Puerto Cabello

La Guaira

TORTUGA

FARALLÓN

Cumaná

CUBAGUA

COCHE

CAR

OCUMARE

PUERTO CRUZ

PUERTO CABELLO

CARACAS

CARENERO HIGUEROTE

GOLFO DE CARIACO

CUMANÁ

Puerto La Cruz

MOCHIMA

I. PÍRITU

PUERTO LA CRUZ

BARCELONA

PUERTO PÍRITU

VENEZUELA

Not to scale.

Ports of Entry

Venezuela:
Güiria
Puerto Cabello
Carúpano
Cumaná
La Guaira
Porlamar
Puerto La Cruz

Carúpano

Güiria

J. Raycroft

Currency

The current form of currency in Venezuela is the Bolívar. The exchange rate varies greatly, so check at time of travel for the exact exchange rate. U.S. dollars are beginning to be accepted, and can be changed easily to local currency. Change houses (called cambios) will also change your money, give money for traveler's checks, and some will give money from credit cards.

Customs and Immigration

Major Ports of Clearance: Güiria, Puerto Cabello, Carúpano, Cumaná, La Guaira, Porlamar and Puerto La Cruz.

Yacht documentation and passports that are up-to-date are necessary at every port. Clearance is usually for up to three months and fees are usually around $50 U.S. You must clear in to every major port, and are allowed to stay at offshore islands en route in or out of Venezuela. It is possible to clear in to one port and out another at the same time in order to freely cruise the ports between. Ask your Customs agent. Please refer to Chris Doyle's Cruising Guide to Venezuela and Bonaire for a list of trustworthy agents and more detailed information of Venezuela's regulations.

Airline Access

Aerotuy	Air Aruba
Air France	Air Margarita
Air Portugal	Alitalia
ALM	American Airlines
Avensa	British Airways
Iberia	KLM
Lufthansa	Swissair
VIASA	Zuliana de Aviacion

Communications

Calling Venezuela from another country:
from the U.S., dial 011 + 58 (country code) + area code (leave off first 0 of area code if applicable) + 7-digit local number
from the U.K., dial 00 + 58 + area code + 7-digit local number
Calling another country from Venezuela:
to the U.S., dial 00 + 1 + area code + 7-digit local number
to the U.K., dial 00 + 44 + city code and local number
Calling within Venezuela:
dial area code + 7-digit local number. If in the same area code, only dial the 7-digit number.

The telephone system in Venezuela is run by CANTV. Cards for pay phones can be bought in CANTV stores, hotels, and some shops. There are also independent communications stations.

Internet Cafés:
Caracas:
Cyber Café Madness, 02-267-1866
Cyber Café Pistach, 02-239-2623
Cybernet, 212-662-2804
Cyberstore, 212-671-9945
Cumana:
Comati, c.a., 093-31-5660
Maracaibo:
Cyberestudio, 061-983181
Porlamar:
Cyberclub Porlamar, 295-263-6465
Puerto La Cruz:
North American Connection, 81-673-186
Puerto Ordaz:
X-net Café, 286-923-3916

Medical Facilities and Emergency Numbers

Police/Ambulance/Fire: 171

For more information on Venezuela, please refer to Chris Doyle's *Cruising Guide to Venezuela and Bonaire*. Contact Cruising Guide Publications at 800-330-9542 or www.cruisingguides.com.

Tourist Office: Puerto La Cruz, 0281-268-8170

Directory of Marinas & Services

Venezuela

Aqua Vi, Puerto La Cruz	0281-263-5544
Astillero & Varadero Del Caribe, Margarita	0295-291-3310
Bahia Redonda Marina, Puerto La Cruz	0281-267-7412
Centro Marino de Oriente, Puerto La Cruz	0281-263-1819
Guanta Marina, Guanta	0281-268-2834
Juan Marina, Porlamar	VHF 72
Los Manglares, Morrocoy	0241-443-0030
Marina Americo Vespucio, Varamar	0281-281-4321
Marina Cumanagoto, Cumaná	0293-431-1423
Marina de Caraballeda, Puerto Azul	0212-288-2712
Marina El Morro, (Imbuca) Puerto La Cruz	0281-281-8880
Marina Maremares, Puerto La Cruz	0281-281-1011
Marina Margarita Yachting, Porlamar	0295-261-0486
Marina Paseo Colón, Puerto La Cruz	0281-265-2563
Marina Puerto Cabello	0242-361-7277
Mi Calichar, Caranero	0212-381-4081
Puerto Azul	0212-372-2415
Puerto Calera	0212-351-5011
Puerto Viejo	0212-352-4044

Directory of Boatyards & Services

Aqua Vi, Puerto La Cruz	0281-263-5544
Astillero de Higuerote, Caranero	0234-323-0625
Astilleros de Oriente, Cumaná	0293-432-1059
Astillero & Varadero Del Caribe, Margarita	0295-291-3310
Bahia Redonda Marina, Puerto La Cruz	0281-267-7412
Marina Americo Vespucio, Varamar	0281-281-4321
Mi Calichar, Caranero	0212-381-4081
Navimca, Cumaná	0293-431-9064
The Navy Yard, Cabello	0242-361-5886
Varadero Caribe, Cumaná	0293-431-0804

S. Scott

J. Raycroft

Directory of Advertisers

CRUISING GUIDE PUBLICATIONS

ORDER FORM
To order, please fill out coupon on back and send check or money order to:
Cruising Guide Publications, P.O. Box 1017, Dunedin, Florida 34697-1017.
For credit card orders only, call 1-800-330-9542 • 1-888-330-9542
E-mail: info@cruisingguides.com • www.cruisingguides.com

❑ $24.95   CRUISING GUIDE TO THE VIRGIN ISLANDS
(11th Edition) by Simon and Nancy Scott. Expanded to include Spanish Virgin Islands.

❑ $24.95   VIRGIN ANCHORAGES (New color aerial photos and color graphics)

❑ $27.95   LEEWARD ANCHORAGES Aerial photos of anchorages from Anguilla
thru Dominica

❑ $24.95   CRUISING GUIDE TO THE LEEWARD ISLANDS — *With GPS
Coordinates* (7th Edition) by Chris Doyle.

❑ $24.95   SAILOR'S GUIDE TO THE WINDWARD ISLANDS
(11th Edition) by Chris Doyle.

❑ $19.95   CRUISING GUIDE TO TRINIDAD AND TOBAGO PLUS BARBADOS
(3rd Edition) by Chris Doyle.

❑ $26.95   CRUISING GUIDE TO VENEZUELA & BONAIRE (2nd Edition)
by Chris Doyle. Provides Anchorage information GPS and full color charts.

❑ $24.95   CRUISING GUIDE TO CUBA — *With GPS Coordinates and Charts*
(2nd Edition) by Simon Charles.

❑ $29.95   GENTLEMAN'S GUIDE TO PASSAGES SOUTH — 7th Edition
With GPS Coordinates — The "Thornless Path to Windward," by Bruce Van Sant.

❑ $15.95   CRUISING GUIDE TO THE SEA OF CORTEZ (From Mulege to La Paz)

❑ $19.95   CRUISING GUIDE TO THE FLORIDA KEYS by Capt. Frank Papy.

❑ $19.95   CRUISING GUIDE TO ABACO BAHAMAS by Steve Dodge. (81/2" x 11")
Containing charts from Walker's Cay south to Little Harbour. *Includes GPS coordinates.*

❑ $27.95   THE BAHAMAS – ABACO PORTS OF CALL AND ANCHORAGES
by Tom Henschel. (11x 8 1/2") Stunning, color aerial photography of the
anchorages of the Abaco Islands.

❑ $10.00   HOME IS WHERE THE BOAT IS by Emy Thomas. A glimpse into the
cruising way of life.

❑ $14.95   THE NATURE OF THE ISLANDS: PLANTS & ANIMALS OF THE
EASTERN CARIBBEAN by Chris Doyle and Virginia Barlow.

❑ $12.95   CARIBBEAN by Margaret Zellers with breathtaking photos by Bob Krist; —
perfect tropical souvenir or gift. Also comes in a hardbound edition for $39.95.
COMPLETE DIVING GUIDE TO THE CARIBBEAN
by Brian Savage and Colleen Ryan. These definitive guides clearly describe
dive sites and stores, with detailed dive plans aided by spectacular color photos.

❑ $29.95   Volume I - The Windward Islands

❑ $29.95   Volume II - The Leeward Islands

❑ $29.95   Volume III - Puerto Rico & The Virgin Islands

❑ $19.95   STORE TO SHORE New from Captain Jan Robinson.– Proven menus from
50 international yacht chefs includes shopping lists, 400 delicious mouthwatering
recipes - cooking and entertaining for every occasion - informal to elegant.

❑ $16.95   SHIP TO SHORE by Jan Robinson (680 recipes and cooking tips from
Caribbean charter yacht chefs.) Jan Robinsons other cook books are described
in full in our catalog and on our web site.

❏ $14.95   RESTAURANT GUIDES AND RECIPE BOOKS: LEEWARD ISLANDS, PUERTO RICO, VIRGIN ISLANDS, CHESAPEAKE BAY, FLORIDA GULF COAST, INTRACOASTAL WATERWAY, (Separate books — $14.95 Each.)

❏ $29.95   CRUISING GUIDE TO CARIBBEAN MARINAS AND SERVICES
This essential reference guide includes details and contact information for marinas and marine repair facilities from the Bahamas through the Caribbean. Don't leave port without it!

❏ $12.00   **CALENDAR**: THE BRITISH VIRGIN ISLANDS.
Photography by Dougal Thornton (New year available in October of preceding year).

❏ $29.95   **VIDEO** (VHS), or (PAL Add $10): SAILING THE WINDWARD ISLANDS by Chris Doyle & Jeff Fisher.

❏ $29.95   **VIDEO** (VHS), or (PAL Add $10): CRUISING THE NORTHERN LEEWARDS by Chris Doyle.

CARIBBEAN YACHTING CHARTS.

Recently surveyed with the yachtsman in mind. Includes GPS coordinates.

❏ $69.00   CYC # 1 Virgin Islands - St.Thomas/Sombrero
❏ $69.00   CYC #2 Northern Leeward Islands - Anguilla/Antigua
❏ $69.00   CYC #3 Southern Leeward Islands - Guadeloupe/Martinique
❏ $69.00   CYC #4 Windward Islands - St. Lucia/Grenada

CALL FOR A COMPLETE CATALOG
or VISIT OUR WEBSITE at cruisingguides.com

ORDER FORM

To order, check the appropriate boxes - fill out coupon and send check or money order to: Cruising Guide Publications, P.O. Box 1017, Dunedin, FL 34697-1017. Florida residents add 7% sales tax. See schedule for shipping charges. All books are shipped within 10 days of receipt of order. Orders only 1-800-330-9542.

SHIPPING & HANDLING:		
For U.S. Orders Totaling	ADD	
Under $15.00	$ 4.00	Larger
$15.01 to 25.99	5.00	orders will
26.00 to 49.99	7.00	be charged
50.00 to 74.99	9.00	according
75.00 to 99.99	10.00	to weight.
Additional Address Add $3.95		

NON-U.S. ORDERS: Orders will be shipped USPS at the lowest available rate. Foreign duties and taxes are the customer's responsibility. It you need a firm shipping cost we will be pleased to fax a quote for airmail versus surface mail shipping on your orders. Fax 727-734-8179.

$ _____ Total Merchandise

$ _____ Sales Tax 7%
Florida Residents Only

$ _____ Shipping & Handling

$ _____ Total Enclosed

Name_____

Address_____

City_____ State_____ Zip_____

Daytime telephone (_____)_____

E-mail_____